FAMILY MATTERS

Perfection Learning

EDITORIAL DIRECTOR   Julie A. Schumacher

SENIOR EDITOR   Terry Ofner

EDITOR   Linda Mazunik

PERMISSIONS   Laura Pieper

REVIEWERS   Larry Bargenquast
Ann Tharnish

DESIGN AND PHOTO RESEARCH   William Seabright and Associates,
Wilmette, Illinois

COVER ART THE BOATING PARTY 1893–94   Mary Cassatt

ACKNOWLEDGMENTS
   "After the Divorce" from *A Night Without Armor* by Jewel Kilcher. Copyright
© 1998 by Jewel Kilcher. Reprinted by permission of HarperCollins Publishers, Inc.
   "As It Is With Strangers" by Susan Beth Pfeffer, copyright © 1989 by Susan
Beth Pfeffer, from *Connections: Short Stories* by Donald R. Gallo, Editor.
Used by permission of Delacorte Press, a division of Random House, Inc.
   From "Birth-Order Blues" by Paula Lynn Parks, reprinted from *Essence*
magazine, November 1995, by permission of the author.
   "The Charmer," from *The Dandelion Garden and Other Stories* by Budge Wilson.
Copyright © 1995 by Budge Wilson. Used by permission of Philomel Books,
a division of Penguin Putnam, Inc.
   "Clear Glass Marbles" by Jane Martin. Copyright © 1982, 1983 by Alexander
Speer, Trustee for Jane Martin. Reprinted by permission of PAJ Publications.
   "Dancer" from *Simple Songs* by Vickie Sears. Copyright © 1990 by Vickie Sears.
Reprinted by permission of Firebrand Books, Ithaca, New York.
   "Father and Son" copyright © 1973, 1998 by the Estate of William Stafford.
Reprinted from *The Way It Is: New & Selected Poems* with the permission of
Graywolf Press, Saint Paul, Minnesota.
   "Gang Girl," originally published in *Essence* magazine as "Gang Girl: The
Transformation of Isis Sapp-Grant" as told to Rosemarie Robotham, August 1998.
Reprinted by permission of the author.   CONTINUED ON PAGE 142

Copyright © 2000 by Perfection Learning Corporation
1000 North Second Avenue, Logan, Iowa 51546
P.O. Box 500, Logan, Iowa 51546-0500
Tel: 1-800-831-4190 • Fax: 1-712-644-2392

Paperback ISBN: 0-7891-5084-0

Cover Craft ® ISBN: 0-7807-9039-1

DOES FAMILY MATTER?

The question above is the *essential question* that you will consider as you read this book. The literature, activities, and organization of the book will lead you to think critically about this question and to develop a deeper understanding of what it means to be in a family and if the family really matters.

To help you shape your answer to the broad essential question, you will read and respond to literature in four sections, or clusters. Each cluster addresses a specific question and thinking skill.

CLUSTER ONE What is a family? **DEFINE**

CLUSTER TWO How are we influenced by family? **COMPARE/CONTRAST**

CLUSTER THREE How do families deal with problems? **EVALUATE**

CLUSTER FOUR Thinking on your own **SYNTHESIZE**

Notice that the final cluster asks you to think independently about your answer to the question—*Does family matter?*

ADAMS' HOUSE
1928
Edward Hopper

FAMILY MATTERS

Possibilities

Today I drove past a house
we almost bought and heard
through the open window music

made by some other family.
We don't make music ourselves, in fact
we define our differences

by what we listen to.
And what we mean by family
has changed since then

as we grew larger then smaller again
in ways we knew would happen
and yet didn't expect.

Each choice is a winnowing,
and sometimes at night I hear
all the possibilities creak open

and shut like screendoors
in the wind,
making an almost musical

accompaniment
to what I know
of love and history.

Linda Pastan

TABLE OF CONTENTS

"They Have to Take You In"

A wealthy man had two sons. The older son was sensible and hardworking, while the younger son was foolish and idle. One day, the younger son asked his father for his share of the family's wealth. The somewhat indulgent father granted his request.

The younger son soon left home for a faraway land, where he recklessly spent all his money. When a famine struck and he was faced with starvation, he took a low paying job feeding pigs. He became so hungry that he was tempted to eat the husks he threw into the pigs' trough. By then, he fully understood his error. "Why, my father's servants are better off than I am now!" he exclaimed.

So the son hurried home. When he met his father, he fell to his knees. "I have done you a terrible wrong," he wept, "and am no longer worthy to be called your son. Make me one of your hired servants. I'll do whatever you command."

Instead, the father joyfully embraced him, clothed him in a fine robe, fitted him with expensive shoes, and gave him a precious ring. Then he called for feasting, music, and dancing.

While this reunion was taking place, the older son had been working in the fields. When he came home, he found the house in an uproar of celebration. Upon learning the cause, he angrily refused to join the feasting. Eventually, the father came outside and asked him what was the matter.

"I've worked for you devotedly for years," the older son complained. "I've never once disobeyed you. But when did you ever give such a feast for me?"

"Son, you are always with me," the father said. "All that I have is yours. It is right that we feast and celebrate. For your brother was dead, and now he's alive! He was lost, and now he's found!"

So ends the biblical story of the Prodigal Son, one of the most famous and moving stories ever told about the family. Most obviously, it celebrates the value of repentance and forgiveness. The young man's humble return is extremely touching—but even more so is the father's joy at his return.

And yet, the story is also weighted with disturbing questions. What about the older son, for whom there has never been such feasting and perhaps never will be? Is he really being treated fairly? The story's ending doesn't suggest that his bitterness has waned. And how can we know whether the younger son is truly reformed? Nothing in the story hints that he came home for any reason other than self-interest. Will he leave again? And if so, will he be forgiven anew if he returns?

All truly great stories about family confront such uncertainties—for more than any other cultural institution, the family is often riddled with questions of love and anger, joy and pain, generosity and jealousy, forgiveness and spite. Given such pressures and conflicts, it is small surprise that people sometimes wonder if the family is endangered. Indeed, it seems likely that few cultures throughout human history have not been anxious for their families. But the fact that families are still with us after untold centuries of wear and tear suggests that they will prevail.

For the family is truly a tough institution—tough and durable. This is because it offers something that we dare not do without, something that the Prodigal Son found that he could rely on. Perhaps the hard-headed Yankee poet Robert Frost captured this essential something when he wrote, "Home is the place where, when you have to go there, / They have to take you in."

CONCEPT VOCABULARY

You will find the following terms and definitions useful as you read and discuss the selections in this book.

adoption legal act of adding an unrelated member to a family

ancestors related family members (before grandparents) back through history

blended family combined family units; stepfamily

descendants those who are born after others and are from a common ancestor

dysfunctional family family with abusive or destructive tendencies

extended family family members who usually do not live under the same roof as the nuclear or immediate family such as grandparents, aunts, uncles, and cousins

family unit a basic unit of society commonly headed by a couple or single parent

foster family a family that nurtures an unrelated child in need of care

genealogy a record of ancestors that come from a common source

generation the time between the parents' births and their children's births

heredity genetic characteristics passed from generation to generation

heritage traditions or property passed from generation to generation

lineage direct descendants from a common ancestor, either through mother's or father's line of kinship

matriarchy a family structure where power and resources are controlled by the mother

mentor trusted counselor or guide

nuclear family another term for "immediate" family which is usually composed of a father, mother and children

patriarchy a family structure where power and resources are controlled by the father

progeny children or offspring

sibling sister or brother

support systems available assistance for the family, including but not limited to extended family members, friends, school, church, government assistance, jobs, child care, and health care

welfare assistance for those in need; usually a cash allowance for necessary items

CLUSTER ONE

What Is a Family?
Thinking Skill DEFINING

Thanksgiving in Polynesia

SUSAN HAVEN

I place my palms on the window ledge of the huge double window in my mom and dad's bedroom, and hoist myself up until I am kneeling on the sill, my nose to the window.

Beyond, and three feet below, is my backyard.

It's not fair. I cleaned my room, I swear I did.

I made my bed, picked up the stuff on the floor, and put all my books in the bookshelf.

But did my mom thank me? Of course not.

Just because I shoved the Monopoly pieces under the bed, along with a couple of nightgowns and maybe two or three CDs that lost their cases, she got mad.

Picky, picky, picky.

First she told me, "I want your room cleaned in an hour," and then when I tried a time-saving plan, like storing stuff under the bed, she didn't appreciate it.

A little bad luck made things even worse.

When she came in to check on me, she stepped barefoot on a little metal Monopoly token.

Wow. Does she scream loud.

I apologized and everything.

But did she forgive me? Of course not.

I'm going to jump out this window, then sneak around the alley and crawl on my stomach past the big kitchen window. My mom's in the

FREEDOM FROM WANT
1943
Norman Rockwell

kitchen right now, with my aunt Rhea, getting the Thanksgiving dinner ready, and I don't want them to see me make my escape.

My aunt is why my mom's in such a bad mood, I know it.

She and my uncle Ted, and their one perfect kid, Andrea (my age, ten and a half) arrived from Chicago this morning.

We're all supposed to break turkey together in about half an hour.

I plan to be in Polynesia. Or at least New Jersey, by then.

Our family is not too fond of their family, but they come every Thanksgiving anyway.

My mom especially dislikes my aunt Rhea. She's rich and snobby and makes my mom and dad and my older brother, Jason, and me feel terrible.

She speaks with an English accent, even though I know she was born right here, where we live, in Massapequa, Long Island, New York.

Whenever Jason or I turn on the TV, Aunt Rhea always asks, oh so sweetly, "My, my, don't you two watch a dreadfully large quantity of television?"

That's the Rhea technique: questions that kill.

Like this morning, she asked Jason, when he was grabbing a cookie from the cookie jar: "Wouldn't you prefer a carrot?"

Who'd prefer a carrot to one of mom's chocolate-chip cookies, anyway?

Or later, as my mom was setting the big table, Rhea came over with the napkins and said: "My, my, Sara, but don't you make Missy or Jason do anything around here?"

Jason calls her Aunt Dia-Rhea.

▲　▲　▲

Unfortunately, my mom brought her into my room to show her how I'd cleaned up before they all arrived, and that's when my mom stepped on the Monopoly top hat. And called me a slob. In front of Aunt Rhea. And told me not to come out until my room was spotless.

My first plan was not to come out of my room until I'm eighteen.

But that didn't seem possible. So I snuck in here, to my parents' bedroom, in the back of the house, and I'm going to climb out this window.

I'd have snuck out of mine, but I left some candies on my window ledge and they melted onto the metal window and now it won't open so easily.

More bad luck.

Besides, I don't want to play with my cousin Andrea anymore.

She is what my grandmother calls "a lovely child."

Andrea offered to set the table.

She always picks up her dishes after a meal and puts them in the sink.

She does the laundry every Saturday.

She compliments everybody on everything.

She doesn't even have to be reminded to do that stuff.

Personally, I think that's sick.

And when we started to play a game of jacks, she slaughtered me. And apologized every move she made.

I press my nose to the window. In the distance, I can see Annie MacElvane's house.

My best friend.

She is probably sitting down to Thanksgiving dinner right now with her warm, friendly family.

I could run away there.

It's not Polynesia, but as my dad would say, I'd make good time. I'd be there in a sec.

The problem is—I can't run anywhere until I get the summer screen out of this window.

I'd rather run away to Polynesia, because it's a great place for kids.

We just studied it in Mrs. Schwartz's Cultures of the World unit.

There's no such word in Polynesia as *my* or *our*. Those are called possessive pronouns. The reason they don't have possessive pronouns is that nobody owns anything, including their own children. Children belong to God and the land and the universe. They have total freedom.

▲ ▲ ▲

According to my map, Polynesia is about six inches from America. Which can't be that far.

I wonder what the kids in Polynesia are like.

I wonder if when they're in school, they have a unit called "The Peoples of Massapequa."

As a token of my friendliness, I'm bringing my jacks along. Mrs. Schwartz says that when you visit other peoples, you should bring a symbol of your own peoples. Jacks should do it. Plus, they'll give me something to do until I make a friend.

Well, the sooner I leave, the sooner I'll be playing tensies in paradise.

Maybe I'll just shove this screen right out the window.

Scrunching down, I kick at it.

Uh oh. A hole. The screen's still attached, but now there's this big hole in it that's the shape of my foot.

If I weren't running away already, I'd seriously consider it now, because when they discover this little disaster I'll be grounded until college.

I'll have to make the hole just a little bigger. Girl size.

Perfect. I'm set.

When my mom and dad realize I'm gone, their hearts will break.

In fact, I think I should write a note to make them feel a little worse. Something like:

Dear Mom and Dad: This home is not working out. If you miss me, call Polynesia 2-4000.

Or:

Personally, I've had enough. I'm going to Polynesia. Don't worry about the sharks there. I'll be fine.

If a shark eats me, that'll really kill them.

My body is easing into the scratchy screen when suddenly I hear a *thud*.

A *thump*.

A *clump*.

And then the rattle and vibration of furniture in the hall.

Heavy footsteps are coming toward the bedroom.

My body stiffens. My heart pounds.

What could that be? I have to get out of here. Fast.

Ow. The torn screen is so scratchy.

Thud. Rattle. Tickle.

Bounce. Bounce.

It's my brother, Jason. Bouncing a basketball in the hall.

When my mom yells at him about indoor basketball bouncing, she has a point. The whole house vibrates.

Is that the doorknob turning? This doorknob?

I try to ease my body further through the screen.

I can't get out.

There's only one thing I can do.

Backing my butt out of the screen, I jump down from the ledge and look around my mom's room for a place to hide.

The closet.

I'll never make it in time.

Diving onto the floor, I roll under the huge queen-sized bed just as the door opens.

In a second, I'm peeking out from under the bedspread, inches from Jason's big clodhopper feet, which are now standing in front of my mom's bureau.

I bet he's looking in the mirror, as usual.

Wait. Those clodhoppers of his are moving. Is he leaving?

No. He's moving toward the window.

I peek out a little further just in time to see him climb onto the ledge, open the window, and kick the screen right out into the backyard.

"What does she want," he's muttering. "I went to the store. I meant to buy regular milk. So I didn't see the label that said buttermilk. Personally, I've had enough!"

His leg is out the window.

My gosh.

He's running away too!

Gee. I'm going to miss him.

What am I talking about—I'm going to miss him? I'm running away too!

Thud. Thud.

It's footsteps again.

What is this? A convention?

You can't even have a little privacy in your own parents' bedroom when you want it.

Jason's heard something too. His head is turned, perked at attention.

The doorknob. It's turning again.

Jason's eyes widen in panic and then he jumps backward off the window ledge.

The next thing I know, I have company under the bed.

"Happy Thanksgiving . . ." I whisper. ·

"Ahhh!" he almost screams in fright, but I cover his mouth as I swallow a giggle, because we can both hear the soft *clip clap* of my mom's loose slippers.

▲ ▲ ▲

She's *clip clapping* around the room. The bureau drawer squeaks open, there's the soft whoosh of something being removed, the drawer squeaks shut again, and then the springs of the mattress hit my nose as she plops down on the bed.

She's sighing. Which lowers the springs even more.

Then she mutters, "Personally I've had enough . . ." and leans backward. "On the other hand, you're a grown woman, Sara. Now, go out there and handle it."

The springs lower, hitting me in the nose, and then lift.

She's gotten up.

In a second, we hear the door open and softly shut.

She's gone.

Wait a second. It's opening again.

"Sara? Are you in here?"

It's my dad, coming in.

But where's my mom, if my dad didn't see her going out?

I know I heard the door shutting.

Oh no. It couldn't be.

But it is.

The door that shut wasn't the bedroom door.

It was the closet door.

My mom, my thirty-five-year-old mom, is hiding in the closet at this very moment.

"Sara? Jason? Missy?" my dad whispers again in a voice that sounds a little lonely.

Gee. Poor Daddy.

He's been stuck out there all alone with Aunt Rhea and Uncle Ted.

Uncle Ted probably just finished showing off his newest gold charge cards to my dad.

I peek out from underneath the bottom of the bedspread.

Everything that's going on is reflected in the full-length mirror on the closet door. I can see a dress caught in the doorjamb of my mom's closet.

She's in there all right.

"Where is everybody?" my dad says.

Silence.

My dad takes one last look around the room, and then moves to the bedroom door again.

▲   ▲   ▲

But just as he's backing out, the closet door opens and my mom pops out.

"Hi . . ." she says.

"Sara! What are you doing in the closet?"

"I was . . . I was looking for a better tablecloth." She swallows and then continues. "Actually, I was also looking for a whole new house. And a whole new me. But . . . it's not in there. . . ." Her face starts to pucker, like she's going to cry.

My dad puts his arm around her.

"Is Rhea getting to you, honey?"

My mom shakes her head. "Nooo. What makes you think that?"

My dad grins.

"And I took it out on the kids. . . ."

"They'll live. . . ." my dad says.

Sure we'll live, I think. But where?

"What's the matter with me?" my mom sobs. "I'm a grown woman. Why does that phony get to me? Why can't I handle it? I have no character. No courage. No strength. You want me to make it all nice. And I try, but she's getting to me. Even your brother Ted is getting to me. All his mutual funds are going up. Did you know that?"

My dad nods. "Sure did."

"Plus, I've been yelling at the kids. For nothing. Well, not nothing. . . ."

Nothing, Mom. Nothing.

"And they're fed up with me. And I don't blame them." She starts to cry again. "The turkey is probably dry, I have an ugly tablecloth, and I'm a terrible mother." She's bawling.

I have to admit that the sound of my mom's sobs is getting to me. I can't help it.

"You're not such a terrible mother . . ." I mumble.

The sobbing stops.

"Who's that? Where's that? What's that?" my mom asks.

"Stevie Baldwin's mom is worse," Jason talks right into the mattress. "She's not as mean as you are today, but she treats him like a baby. Last week, four guys were playing pool in his room, and she walks in, and with this high, squeaky voice, says 'Would any of you boys like a Twinkie . . .?' You'd never do that!"

Just as Jason's finishing his speech the bedspread, like a curtain, rises, and my mom's wide eyes stare at us.

"Happy Thanksgiving," I say to her. Then, I can't help adding, "But for next Thanksgiving, you ought to dust under here, Mom. . . ."

She blushes. Then her thumb jerks backward, like a hitchhiker.

"Out. Both of you. Out."

Jason rolls one way. I roll the other.

In a second we're all standing around my mom and dad's bed.

My mom's fingertips are against her cheeks. I think she's in shock. My dad's eyes have already taken in the open window.

Just as I say, "Jason was running away," Jason says, "Missy was running away."

And then we both say, "We can't take it anymore either."

My dad and mom give each other looks. I feel lectures and meaningless sayings coming on.

"Aunt Rhea means well . . ." my mom begins.

But now that we know how she really feels about Aunt Rhea, all we have to do is give her a "yeah, sure" look, and she stops.

"On the other hand, kids . . ." Now my dad is going into speech mode. "You can't run away from a problem . . ."

But then he looks at my mom, who is standing inches from her former hideaway closet.

▲ ▲ ▲

And he stops. And sighs. "What are we going to do?" he says. "They are unbearable. I've tried to talk to them, hint, be diplomatic, but it's like talking to Martians . . ."

Everyone's looking dumb, so I jump right in there. "Could we . . . *all* run away?" I ask softly.

All our eyes shift to the open window. Then we look at each other.

I can see the open sea. Polynesia. Palm trees.

Then my dad sighs. "My mother, your grandmother, would have a heart attack in heaven. . . . I can't . . ."

My mom agrees. "Look, it's a Thanksgiving from hell . . . but otherwise it's not so terrible. What we have to do is what we do every year. Get through it, and give thanks on Sunday—when it's over."

Everybody nods at practically the same time. Which makes us all giggle.

"Are we ready?" my dad asks. "We have to get out there or they're going to start to get suspicious. Plus, the turkey is done. . . ."

My mother turns white. "Oh no . . . my turkey . . . my turkey." She lunges for the door.

Then she stops, pauses, looks back at us, puts a big smile on her face, stands up straight, and with dignity, walks out her bedroom door.

My father follows.

My brother goes next.

Before I leave, I take one last peek at the window.

I guess that's what people mean by a window of opportunity.

Polynesia would have been swell.

But it's not to be.

Of course, Christmas is coming up and there are rumors that my mother's second cousins are coming up from Florida.

I can feel the wind wafting through my hair already.

But in the meanwhile, I close the door behind me, take a deep breath, and gather up the courage that the Peoples of Massapequa are known for. ❧

I Am Singing Now

LUCI TAPAHONSO

the moon is a white sliver
balancing the last of its contents
in the final curve of the month

my daughters sleep
in the back of the pickup
breathing small clouds of white in the dark
they lie warm and soft
under layers of clothes and blankets
how they dream, precious ones, of grandma
and the scent of fire
the smell of mutton[1]
they are already home.

i watch the miles dissolve behind us
in the hazy glow of taillights
and the distinct shapes of hills and mesas[2] loom above
then recede slowly in the clear winter night.

i sing to myself
and think of my father
    teaching me, leaning toward me
    listening as i learned.
    "just like this," he would say
    and he would sing those old songs

        into the fiber of my hair,
        into the pores of my skin,
        into the dreams of my children

and i am singing now
for the night
    the almost empty moon
    and the land swimming beneath cold bright stars.

1 **mutton:** meat of sheep
2 **mesas:** flat-topped hills

Gary Paulsen and friend

Nativity

GARY PAULSEN

It came in a wild storm, the litter, which did not help to lessen my concern.

I had carefully noted the day when the puppies were conceived and knew that Cookie was as regular as a clock—sixty-five days—when it came to gestation.

But sixty-five days put us smack in the middle of January. January in northern Minnesota is—literally—a hard time. Everything is brittle, difficult. It is paradoxically the very best time to run dogs because it is cuttingly cold—which the dogs love and work best in—and the snow is clean and deep enough to be easy on the sleds.

Everything else is hard. At forty, fifty below, vehicles don't start, tires freeze and break, pipes—even those protected by straw and buried deep—freeze solid. Hot water must be carried to the dogs, who dehydrate[1] in the dry air of winter, and the old water must be literally chopped out of their pans with an ax. The water is mixed with beef blood to lure them into drinking it fast before it freezes again—within eight or nine minutes—and this process must be done twice a day while running team after team to train for the race and cooking dog food each evening to feed the next day.

And in the middle of January, when it is the busiest, when there is no time, not a minute to spare, and everything is pushed to the absolute limit of its performance envelope—smack in the middle—there came one of the worst blizzards I had ever seen.

1 **dehydrate:** dry out

It roared down from the North, driven by a dropping cold front called an Alberta Clipper. The winds kicked up to sixty, seventy miles an hour and the true temperature, with driven snow, dropped to forty below—windchill making it close to a hundred below.

Just feeding the dogs became difficult, almost impossible. We had forty-some dogs then and I used a snowmobile to pull a freight sled loaded with dog food out to the kennel and run down the rows of dogs to feed them. It was so dark and the driving snow made visibility so bad that twice I missed the kennel altogether and wound up stuck in the woods west of the dogs. It was the kind of storm you often read about but never see—except this time it was real.

And at the high point, at the very worst peak of the meanest part of the storm, Cookie was due to have her puppies.

My worry turned to something on the edge of panic. She was in her doghouse, her chain disconnected and fresh straw fluffed in, but the storm was so intense I did not see how she could keep the puppies—they are, of course, wet when they come—from freezing solid.

I thought of moving her into the house, but it would be too warm and unhealthy. The dogs' winter coats were in full prime by then, and being in a warm room could do worse than sicken them, it could kill a winter dog to bring him in. The heat would be murderous.

The solution came as I ran the snowmobile past the stack of straw bales by the kennel: If I could not take Cookie to a house, I would bring the house to her.

It was by this time midafternoon and nearly dark, so I left the snowmobile running to use the headlight and carried straw bales to her circle in the kennel.

I constructed a "house" from these straw bales. It took twenty-two bales and a couple of flat boards to hold the roof bales up, but when it was done it was snug and out of the wind and large enough for Cookie and me.

While building I had decided the only way I would get any relief from my anxiety was to stay with her. I smoothed the snow in the bottom of the shelter and spread out fluffed straw almost a foot thick. I had left an igloolike opening just large enough to crawl through, which I could plug with straw after we were inside, then I went to the house and brought a thermos of tea, another of soup, my headlamp, a book to read, my sleeping bag and foam pad, and we moved in.

I had some concern that Cookie would not like it, would prefer her own doghouse, but I needn't have worried. She entered, smelled the straw, peed in one corner to mark it, and made a birth bed in another.

I pulled my gear in, plugged the opening, and unrolled my bag.

"Nice," I said. "Way better than we're used to . . ."

Cookie was busy licking herself and didn't respond—although she usually did. We talked often, sometimes at great length; I frequently explained parts of my life to her, which sometimes helped me understand myself better, and if she didn't know all the words (actually, she did recognize many individual words) she was a master at tones. She could tell by the sound of my voice if I was happy, sad, angry, distracted, worried, unsure, positive, lying, telling the truth, if I truly believed in what I was saying or needed to be argued with to be certain. A hundred, a thousand times a year we "negotiated" differences—when and where to best go—and almost invariably she was right.

And I was not exaggerating when I said it was better than we were accustomed to sleeping in. We had spent years, thousands of miles alone together, camping in rain and open storms, on ice and mud; sleeping huddled under an overhang of snow or dirt or on a frozen riverbed; and sometimes resting by just standing still for a moment—taking a whole night's sleep standing against a tree for four minutes.

An insulated straw house was a palace.

Our combined body heat quickly warmed the inside of the shelter and I feared that it would get too warm. But I opened the straw plug and let some cool air in—kept it at about forty degrees (above zero) and leaned back in the straw to wait for the pups.

Of course, they did not hurry. When you want them to come, they take forever. They only hurry when you aren't ready, never when you are prepared.

I poured a cup of tea and leaned back against the straw, my legs in the sleeping bag, my headlamp adjusted down for reading, and settled in to spend the night with Cookie and Anthony Trollope.[2] I had for some time wanted to read *The Pallisers* and this looked like a good time to at least start.

It had been a long day, however, and the wind tearing by outside and the warmth (a full eighty degrees warmer than out in the wind) made the little bale house seem even more cozy. My eyes closed, opened, closed again, and stayed closed.

I awakened some four hours later. My batteries had run down, so the headlamp gave only a soft glow and for a second I didn't remember where I was; then I heard the sound . . . and knew.

Cookie had decided to go on without my dubious aid and was giving birth. I pulled out of the bag and moved over to her in a crouch.

I'm not sure what I meant to do. She was certainly fine without my help, had done it many times before, and was as I have stated an excellent mother. I was more a hindrance than a help, and I held slightly back to give her room for her work.

She was on the fourth one. The first three—all a gray color like Cookie—were out and cleaned and dry and working at finding a nipple, making the small sounds of new puppies, the tiny whine-grunt that seems to come more from their fat little bodies than their mouths.

The smell filled the shelter. I always thought it smelled new—fresh puppy smell, milk smell, new smell—and I petted Cookie and touched the pups to get man-smell on them so they would come to know it as

2 **Anthony Trollope:** 19th-century author of the Victorian novel series, *The Pallisers*

part of their mother. Many females would not let you touch their pups, would take a piece out of you if you did, but Cookie was milder—at least with me. (I had seen her rip a man's hand when he jumped around the side of her house and said "Boo!" as a practical joke. He took stitches and could never get close to her again without experiencing Cookie's low growl and her lips coming up to show teeth.) But she didn't mind having her puppies handled as long as she could see them.

I picked each pup up, rolled it in my hand to determine sex—although it didn't matter to me which they were. (Females tend to lead better, males usually pull harder—so it all works out.) So far they were all males, and I put them back on nipples and got ready for the next one.

Seven pups, all gray and fat and healthy—little Cookies—all smelling new and milky and warm, and then the eighth and last one came, and it was stillborn.

She worked at it. When I saw she was having trouble I reached in, thinking it hadn't cleared its nostrils or took air too late—I had done miniature CPR on other puppies and gotten them breathing—but it was too late. It must have died in the birth canal or just before, and there was nothing we could do. Cookie licked harder and harder, trying to get it to breathe, her actions becoming more and more frantic.

"It's no use," I said aloud. "This one didn't make it . . ."

She growled concern and it turned to a whine, and I reached one hand to cover Cookie's eyes and with the other I took the pup and moved it near the door opening. Cookie had never had a dead pup before, but with other females I had done this, hidden the dead one and then taken it away and it had worked. They focused on the live ones and forgot the dead one.

But this was Cookie. I should have known. Cookie was not like other dogs. She was easily the most strong-willed person—and I mean *person*—I had ever met. Once when she'd taken a load of porcupine quills in her face, I'd rushed her to the vet to have her put out so we could pull them, and she simply would not go down. The vet gave her two full doses of anesthetic and it didn't put her out at all. On the third dose she sat, her butt on the table, but was still conscious and ready to bite any hand that came at her. The vet was afraid to give her more, but the drugs slowed her enough so we could pull a quill, then dodge before she hit us.

Stubborn, immensely strong-willed and powerful, and completely, totally dedicated—this wasn't just another dog, it was Cookie.

She looked for the pup with her nose, pushing the others out of the way, tumbling them, trying to find the dead one, and when she couldn't find it, she looked at me.

None of this side-looking stuff, none of this looking up and then away, none of this I-don't-want-to-threaten-you dog-man looks. This was a look from a mother with a missing baby, a look aimed directly, fiercely, hotly into my eyes, into my soul.

Where is it?

It was as clear as if she'd asked it. And I knew that I had almost no time to find the pup and give it back. It was no longer man and dog—if, indeed, it had ever been thus with Cookie and me. It was now mother and intruder, mother and possible kidnapper, mother and fool. She would take me, tear me apart, and there was no doubt anywhere in the shelter. I reached under the straw and started to hand it over, but she reached for it, took it gently in her mouth, and set it on the straw and began working on it again, nudging it with her nose, licking it with hard strokes, trying to get it to breathe, to move, while making small whines. I think she knew, really knew, that it was hopeless but could not let it go, would not let it go.

The other pups nursed and she checked on them at intervals—every two, three minutes—but kept working on the dead puppy and when she could not get it to respond no matter what she did, she picked it up and put it with the other pups to nurse.

She watched it carefully and the movement of the other pups caused the body of the dead one to move and she must have thought it alive because she lay back, exhausted from the birthing, and closed her eyes and went to sleep.

I waited a full minute, then carefully reached over and removed the dead pup. While Cookie still slept, I crept out of the hut and put the body of the pup some twenty yards away in a snowbank. I didn't want to leave Cookie yet and planned to spend the night or at least stay until I was sure the rest of the pups were all right, and I thought she would not find the body there. I pushed it into the snow and covered it, and then stole back to the shelter, rearranged the plug and unrolled my sleeping bag, and went to sleep. I would take care of the body of the pup when I went to the house.

I had become exhausted and when I next awakened, the wind had abated[3] and I could see daylight coming through the crack in the opening.

3 **abated:** grew less

I turned on my headlamp and scanned the interior of the bale house and saw that Cookie was still fast asleep. I was getting ready to leave when I saw a strange lump.

There, in the middle of the puppies, lay the frozen body of the dead pup, stuck back into a nursing position.

Without awakening me, Cookie had gotten up during the night, gone out, found the pup and brought it back, arranged it to "feed" with the others, and gone back to sleep.

I was caught somewhere between heartbreak and admiration, and I thought suddenly of orphan children I had seen in the streets in Juárez, Mexico, back in the early sixties and how it would have been for them to have such a mother, such a wonderful mother.

Cookie slept hard, was absolutely sound asleep, and I thought I would take the body now, take it to the house and dispose of it so she could not find it. But when I reached across the hut to get it, her eyes opened and her lips moved to clear teeth, and again she looked directly into my eyes.

I will pull your sled, she said, *and love you and lead the team and save your life and be loyal to all that you are and obey you in all things until I cannot, but if you touch my pup you die.*

I left the pup and it was not for three days, almost four, when the still-frozen pup was clearly not going to come back to life, that she finally surrendered to her grief and let me take it away.

But even then she growled, this time not at me but at the fates, at all of it. That she would lose a young one—a growl at life. ❧

Isis Sapp-Grant as photographed by Gordon Parks

Gang Girl

ISIS SAPP-GRANT
AS TOLD TO ROSEMARIE ROBOTHAM

Her mother named her Isis, after the Egyptian goddess of fertility and pro-tection, and, indeed, the young woman with waist-length dreads[1] was once an adolescent to whom other teenagers paid a kind of homage—and money for protection. She has become a woman since then—a statuesque beauty, her cheekbones finely etched, her dark eyes slanted upward, her skin a deep polished brown. Today Isis Sapp-Grant laughs easily, and yet there is a ghost of sadness on the high plane of her forehead, an unsurprised wari-ness in the depths of her eyes. A decade ago, she was the female leader of one of New York City's most notorious high-school gangs, the Deceptinettes, and violence was the routine of her day. Isis has become a clinical social worker whose primary focus is young gang members. Though her history still pains her, she views it as the fire in which her life's purpose was forged. She shares her story in the hope that it will help others understand the forces that lure teenagers into the deadly spiral of gang violence.

I didn't set out to join, let alone start, one of the most fearsome girl gangs in the city. But there I was. Me and my girls, the Deceptinettes, sisters of the male Decepticons—Decepts for short. The name was inspired by a silly Saturday morning cartoon, *Transformers*, which pitted the Decepticons, who were the bad guys, against the Autobots, who were the law enforcers.

This was 1986, and I was 15 years old, living in Brooklyn with my mother, who was a social worker, and my three sisters, who at the time

---

1 **dreads:** thin hair braids or mats

were 18, 14 and 2. My father wasn't around much; he and my mother were divorced. I'd just started at the High School of Graphic Communication Arts in Manhattan. My sisters were at different schools and, fortunately, they never got pulled into gangs. My personality was just different from theirs. I was more of a scrapper, always challenging my mother. As a kid, I thought I knew everything; I felt so powerful inside, and I couldn't understand why my mother didn't *see* that. She'd say, "Isis, why you always trying to act bigger than you are?" I craved recognition. So by high school, I was ripe for anything that would give me that feeling of power. And that turned out to be Decept.

The Decepticon gang started in the early 1980s at Brooklyn Tech, one of the top high schools in New York City. The male gang leader, Derek, aka Megatron, became my boyfriend at one point. He was an honor student before he eventually got shot in the head and became paralyzed. Like Derek, when I first got into Decept, I didn't have a clue I'd be in for that kind of violence. I was mostly thinking about protecting myself.

I realized quickly that there were a lot of violent kids at school. But if I acted crazy, they kept their distance. And I found that the crazier I acted, the more respect I got. Some of the other girls who were new to the school noticed it, too, and started hanging with me. We weren't really a gang. Just friends. But we let it be known that if you messed with us, we would fight back. And that's how it started. There were about ten of us in the beginning, but soon more girls joined us, and other kids in the school began giving us money to protect them. A lot of us lived in Brooklyn and knew some of the Decepticons. They would back us up in fights sometimes. After a while, we decided to officially join forces with the guys and call ourselves Deceptinettes.

Our ranks grew to about 70 over the next three years—that's how long I stayed in the gang. In all, there were several hundred Decept members, mostly male, at high schools throughout the city. We called our main headquarters—Derek's school—Cybertron, like in the cartoon, and our favorite gathering place was this park we called Signs of the Times. We even had a hand signal that we copied from the cartoon. In the beginning, Decept meetings were just a group of mostly Black and Hispanic teenagers hanging with their friends. The only problem was, to get respect on the street, we had to act bad. And things just escalated from there.

The first time I ever robbed someone was on Halloween, a couple of months after I started high school. On this particular day, 50 or more

Decepts decided to cut class and congregate in the park. And everybody was drinking Cisco[2] and getting restless and mean. The next thing I remember, we went down into the nearby subway station and started racing up and down the platform and through the trains, robbing people, grabbing their stuff, beating them up if they resisted. I did it, too. I felt no boundaries, just this mad adrenaline rush. And at the time, I really liked the feeling that no one could mess with me. That I was invincible. Anything I wanted was *mine*.

I went home that evening with rings and gold chains and Louis Vuitton bags,[3] and my mother didn't even notice. I knew she was having her own problems. I think she was depressed. Even though she had been a good mother to me and my sisters till then, she wasn't really paying attention to what I was getting into. And my sisters took their cue from her and left me alone.

That night I spread on my bed all the stuff I had stolen, and I was just amazed. I thought, *That was too easy.* After that, the violence really kicked in. And once it started, we couldn't stop because people were looking to get revenge on us, so we had to keep fighting just to protect ourselves. Plus, I think we really wanted to hurt people—as terrible as that sounds. We would play this game called one-punch knockout: We'd stand outside the subway station and choose somebody and try to knock them out with one punch. I was good at that. Or we would sit around outside the school—we hardly ever went inside for classes anymore—and come up with ways to just mess with folks. By then, our rep had gotten so far out there that most people just gave us whatever we wanted. It was at the point where we could close down any school by calling the school office and telling them Decepts were coming. People were that scared.

But they *needed* to be scared. We would get *high* on the violence. People were getting killed over the most stupid stuff. I remember the first time I saw somebody die. We had beat up this boy's sister, and that night we were partying at some club. People were high out of their minds, and here comes this boy talking about "Leave my sister alone." This Jamaican guy I had a crush on—Frankie—he's like, "Just go away, man. You don't know what you're getting into. Just go." But the boy wouldn't leave, and some of the Decept girls started hitting him with

2 **Cisco:** brand of cheap beer
3 **Louis Vuitton bags:** expensive brand of ladies' handbags

baseball bats and hammers. Then the guys came outside and jumped into it, and one minute I saw the boy, the next minute I couldn't. They were just totally *stomping* him! Some guys fired shots, and all I remember was seeing the blood and thinking, *This is all over hitting some stupid little girl.*

I didn't know what to feel that night. I ran—we all ran—and found my way home in a blur. After a time, though, it didn't even matter. When you're in a gang, you see so much blood that you don't even care. It's

almost like being a nurse. I would come home with blood on my shoes, blood on my coat, and my mother would say, "Where'd you get that coat?" And I'd say, "My friend gave it to me." Always some excuse. Then I'd go wash the blood off, wash my cuts and bruises—I never did get shot, thank God—and I'd think, *she doesn't even see what's going on.*

The way I felt was, no one cared about me and so I wasn't going to care about them. That's why I could watch somebody cry, plead, bleed, and it wouldn't touch me. It was as if we were all on a giant totem pole, and Black people were at the very bottom, and I was totally invisible. When you feel as invisible as I felt, you can become the most dangerous person in the world because you don't even care about your own life. I knew I wasn't going to live past 18. The only thing that gave me any pride was the fact that I was in Decept.

We actually had some very smart guys and some very intelligent and beautiful girls in Decept. One girl, Tangee, had been valedictorian[4] of her junior-high-school class, and her parents bought her everything she wanted. But she was still missing something, and she was looking for it with us. Every one of us was troubled in some way. I was missing the mother I had known as a little girl. I had watched my mother struggling to raise us, and she was just beaten down from it, beaten down by life. She stayed inside her room most of the time. I didn't understand what was going on with her. She still went to her job every day, but when she came home she would withdraw, like she didn't really care what I was into. And I was so angry.

Another Decept girl, Nelsa, was the daughter of a heroin addict, and she had been taking care of her mother and younger siblings from the time she was 13 by working as a stripper. She would come from the club to school with a bagful of money, a fur coat and a gun. My best friend, Lisa, had been born in jail. She shuttled between foster care and her mother's house till she was 8. While living with her mother, she was abused—she actually looked forward to going back into foster care. Lisa could be just cold. If you messed with her in any way, she could hurt you without blinking.

Surprisingly, Lisa is now a high-school special-ed teacher, and a mother and wife. And Nelsa stopped stripping two years ago, started college and got a job in marketing. Lisa and Nelsa and me, we all got out. Tangee didn't. Tangee became a crackhead.[5] I think of her now, wasted and strung out and abused, and I realize that could have been me. Except I never did crack. I wasn't into hard drugs like some of the other Decepts. I would smoke marijuana, and we all drank to get ourselves hyped up for whatever we had to do, but thank God I had the sense to stay away from cocaine.

The other thing was, I stayed a virgin. Lisa did, too. There were so many diseases out there, and we had been in so many abortion clinics

---

4 **valedictorian:** student with highest grade point average

5 **crackhead:** person addicted to crack cocaine

with our Decept sisters, we wanted no part of sex. . . . All that fighting and stealing eventually got me arrested, of course. When I turned 16, I was picked up for robbing some girl on the subway. I remember being handcuffed and taken to jail by these two Black undercover cops who must have been the most gorgeous men I had ever seen in my life. And I was so embarrassed. The handcuffs were like chains around my wrists. I felt like a slave. In my head, I kept saying, *This is not you. You are not really like this.* But then this other thought kept coming: *Don't fool yourself, Isis. This is you.*

I was in jail for a week and a half. I called my mother from the precinct house. She said, "Little girl, these people you're running with, they are *not* your friends. You *have* no friends. Your only friends are your family." But I still didn't get it. I thought Decept was my family. I loved my Decept sisters and brothers. We would do things that families did, like go to the beach and have picnics, baby showers and dance parties.

But we also went to funerals together. Members of Decept were dying all the time. Others of us were drug addicts, still others were in jail with life sentences, and some girls had two, three babies with no-account guys. I was getting tired of losing everybody one by one, and, beneath all the toughness, I was hurting.

By age 17, I was going to funerals *every week*. And then Frankie got shot. He was my heart. Walking home after his funeral, I told myself, *This does not matter.* But that night I went into my mother's room and climbed into her bed. I needed to reach out in the dark and know she was there.

The whole night I dreamed about Frankie. The next morning I thought I was still dreaming because my mother was standing over me, and I had the weird sensation that she was looking down at me in my casket. She was crying. She said, "Isis, I want you to live. I want you to *choose* to live. I don't want to bury you ten feet under. I want to see your children."

From that day, things began to change. I started showing up for more classes so I wouldn't get into trouble. But sometimes I'd just want to be with my friends, and stuff would start happening. If I said, "I'm going home," they'd be like, "Isis, you're selling us out."

When I did go to class, a couple of my teachers began taking an interest. One was my writing teacher, a Black man named Mr. Mason. He encouraged me to write about what I was going through in the gang. The other one was Mrs. Beasley, a tough little seventysomething Black woman. Most teachers at my high school were scared to death of me, but not Mrs. Beasley. She would challenge me to try harder.

One other person helped save my life: a cop! The first time John Galea saw me, the cops had pulled me in for a lineup; he cussed me out, called me a little hoodlum. But he saw something else in me too, because he kept telling me, "Isis, you're smart. You can do better."

So these three people hooked up with my mother and the principal of the school, and they came up with a plan. They told me that if I would go to class and keep out of trouble, they would allow me to graduate. They arranged for me to attend Fisk University, the well-known Black school in Nashville. We knew I had to get out of New York because all these people who knew I didn't have Decept protection anymore were calling my house every day, threatening my family. As long as I was there, my mother and sisters weren't safe.

Well, I graduated. I went to Fisk and cooled my heels for a year. But I just didn't fit in. People in Nashville still saw me as this bad New York City gang girl. I wasn't that person anymore. My consciousness had changed.

So after a year I transferred to the State University of New York at Stony Brook, Long Island. I met my husband-to-be, Alphonzo Grant, there, a big football-playing, clean-living jock who is now a lawyer. He was so sweet to me, even after I told him my history. I think he fell in love with me because by then I had started to fall in love with myself. I was taking good care of myself, studying hard, majoring in social work. And I meditated and prayed a lot. I was beginning to understand that God had a plan for me. After college, I got married and later went on to earn a master's degree in social work at New York University. Life can be amazing.

Still, I regret all the hurt I caused. People come up to me even now with scars on their faces or bodies, and they'll say, "Isis, do you remember me?" Some of them actually laugh when they say that, but most of them are really bitter. Like the woman I met in a store where I was buying shoes for my first job interview.

This woman holding a baby comes up to me and tears are running down her face, and she has this scar on her cheek and she says, "Isis, you don't know me, do you? You don't even remember what you did to me." And the horrible thing was, I *didn't* remember. I told her, "Whatever I did to you, I'm so, so sorry." She just stood there, crying and shifting the baby from hip to hip, and when she saw I still didn't remember, she said, "If I didn't have this baby with me, I'd kill you right now." And she walked out of the store.

There are faces I still see in my dreams, people we fought with who I later heard had died. I felt responsible because I was a part of the violence that killed them. But I can't change what I did. All I can do now is try to give back, try to make good on this promise I made to God: I promised that if I got out of my teens alive, if God spared me, I'd use my life to help save kids like me.

These days I do one-on-one therapy with kids at risk for involvement in gangs. I get referrals through the Madison Square Boys and Girls Club, and I work with the House of the Lord Church's community outreach program in Brooklyn. I do workshops in schools, and I travel the subways a lot and talk to the kids, because most New York City gangs still operate out of the subways. A whole new generation of Decepts is out there now, as well as other groups like the Latin Kings, the Crips and the Bloods.

I work mostly with gang girls; boys with these issues do better with male mentors. The truth is, every boy and girl out here needs a mentor to help them see what choices they can make, what programs they can participate in. If you're going to tempt these kids away from the thrill of violence—and violence can be an incredible high—you have to make them understand that somebody cares about them, that they are not invisible or powerless, that their life *means* something.

Parents in particular need to lay down clear guidelines, give their kids lots of reinforcement, and, most of all, pay attention to who their kids are becoming, who their kids' friends are, what interests them. None of us is perfect. We all get worn down by life sometimes. But we have no choice but to keep on trying to reach our children.

Looking back I see that my own mother never stopped caring, though she didn't always know how to help me. And the most important thing she ever did for me was to stand at my bedside that morning after Frankie's funeral, challenging me to live. ∾

RESPONDING TO CLUSTER ONE

WHAT IS A FAMILY?

Thinking Skill DEFINING

1. Write three words to **define**, or describe, the families in each of the selections in this cluster. Try not to repeat the defining words you use. You might use a chart such as the one below.

Title	Three Words to Describe the Family
Thanksgiving in Polynesia	
Nativity	
I Am Singing Now	
Gang Girl	

2. The father in "Thanksgiving in Polynesia" says, "You can't run away from a problem." Look at Cookie in "Nativity." How does her "growl at life" relate to the father's outlook on life?

3. The speaker in "I Am Singing Now" remembers the songs her father taught her. What song or story have you learned from parents or relatives that you could pass on to the next generation?

4. Name at least three things that Isis gives up to be part of a gang family. In your opinion, is a gang really a family? Why or why not?

Writing Activity: Defining a Familiy

Create your own definition of a family. The chart from Question one above might provide information you could use in your definition. Write your definition as either prose or poetry.

A Strong Definition

- begins by stating the term to be defined
- lists the various characteristics or qualities of the term
- provides examples
- ends with a final definition

CLUSTER TWO

How Are We Influenced by Family?

Thinking Skill   COMPARING AND CONTRASTING

The Charmer

BUDGE WILSON

I am thirty-three years old now, and I no longer wake up each morning with a hard lump of anger pressing against my chest.

It seems I've come full circle. Way back when I was a little girl, I was not angry at all, not ever. Like everyone else, I was too charmed to be irritated. No. But perhaps *charmed* is too mild a term. At that age, I felt something more intense. I was bewitched. My heart lay open and eager. He could take it and me, and do with us what he would. When he beckoned, I followed, at top speed. If he said, "How about you wash my bike for me, Posie, love?" I would be halfway to the kitchen for a bucket and rags before he stopped speaking. When he said, "Go get my baseball, kid," I ran and got it. "Thanks, Posie," he'd say, grabbing the ball and disappearing to the park.

My name is not Posie. It's Winnifred. Winnifred means "friend of peace." Later I would have a grim laugh or two about that. He always called me Posie when he wanted me to do something for him, or when he wished to make it clear to me that I had measured up. It was payment for good behavior, and an insurance policy for future services. Collect his baseball and I will get my reward—his flashing Colgate smile and my pet name.

He was my brother.

His name was Zackary, and he was eleven years older than I was. Wouldn't you know they'd call him Zackary and me Winnifred? Zackary has such an exotic ring to it, and when all his friends took to calling him Zack, it was like he was a movie star or a TV hero or something. It has always seemed to me that the most compellingly male, the most electric movie and rock stars, have short names. I watch a lot of late-night movies on the tube, and I should know. Clark Gable, John Wayne, Kirk Douglas, Steve McQueen. And nearer to the present day, Mick Jagger, John Lennon, Matt Dillon. Take Tyrone Power,[1] now. A lot of women have admired Tyrone Power. But to my way of thinking, he was as flimsy, as pretty, as his name.

But Winnifred. Winnifred is on a par with Edna, Maud, Ernestine—terrible names, all of them. It's true that, for a while, I thought that Winnifred might be special. In Sunday school, we had a hymn that went:

Winnie cometh, Winnie cometh,
To make up His jewels . . .

The hymns were thrown onto a screen, in huge block letters, and at first I was too young to read the words. What delicious prestige to be that Winnie who everyone was singing about! Placed in a hymn and written on the wall for all to see. Chosen to become His jewels—rubies, diamonds, opals. Then, of course, I learned to read, and found out the truth.

When He cometh, when He cometh,
To make up His jewels . . .

And I realized I'd be precious lucky to be even one of those jewels. Besides, I wasn't really Winnie, anyway. I was Winnifred. Don't ask me why, but I just wasn't the kind of kid who ended up with a nickname. So you can imagine the effect that "Posie" had upon my spirit. As early as three years old, I knew that posies were a bouquet of flowers.

▲ ▲ ▲

I was Zackary's willing slave. Slavery, in fact, was in vogue in our house. Mom would make a chocolate layer cake for the church bazaar and leave it on the kitchen table with a sign beside it: FOR CHURCH BAZAAR. DEATH TO ANYONE WHO TOUCHES IT. Chances are she'd arrive home from town, two hours before the bazaar, to find a large piece cut out of the side, crumbs all over the floor, and the sign turned upside down.

Then Zack would come home just as she was tying on her apron to make another cake. Brown from the sun, black curls glistening from the municipal pool, he would enter the kitchen, dancing a little jig on the doormat. His mouth would go all mock-sad and quivering at the corners.

1 **Tyrone Power:** American actor (1914-1958)

"My mother, my queen!" he might say. "How could someone with any taste buds at all ignore the creation of so great a cook? The master chef of the whole of this city!" Then he would give her one of his special bear hugs. Or he might get down on one or even both of his knees. "Forgive me, Duchess," he would say, and then unbutton his shirt, laying bare his marvelous brown chest. "For the knife," he would say. "For death."

Then my mother would laugh, we'd *all* laugh, and Mom would mix up the batter for the new cake, a smile playing upon her lips. "Go ahead!" she'd say, with a fake sigh. "Have another piece. You certainly are the limit!" My two little sisters and I would stand there grinning, while Zack sat down and ate half the cake. Then the three of us would wash up the old baking dishes and the new baking dishes and his plate and fork and glass. And sweep up his crumbs. Before he left, he would probably bow low once more to Mom, and say, "Thank you, my angel." She'd put her head on one side, with that adoring look of hers, and say, "Be off with you! You're a real devil!"

Which, of course, he was. But anyone who knows anything about devils knows that they're fallen angels, and can often fool you for a very long time. We studied a chunk of *Paradise Lost*[2] in grade twelve. Milton's Satan certainly had a lot more going for him than the angels who hovered over the garden, exuding piety.

Even Dad took a long time to wake up. You wouldn't think a fourteen- or sixteen-year-old boy could hoodwink a father, but he could, he could. Zack lied over trifles, and periodically stole money out of wallets that were left lying around. He started smoking at thirteen, and was into the liquor cabinet by fourteen. At sixteen, he smashed up our car one night after a poker party. Once he dumped Dad's red toolbox, tools and all, in the river, during one of his rages. The toolbox seemed to bother Dad even more than the car. But afterwards, Zack would deliver apologies that would have brought tears to a preacher's eyes. That kind of dramatic repentance has a lot more clout than simple everyday good behavior, and he really knew how to pull it off. Zack'd been in Sunday school himself long enough to be able to quote from the Prodigal Son[3] on appropriate occasions, and for the first twenty-two or so times he did it, he really convinced us when he said he was "no longer worthy

---

2 *Paradise Lost:* poem by John Milton

3 **Prodigal Son:** story in the Bible in which a son runs away only to return begging forgiveness from his father

to be called thy son." The part about making him "one of thy hired servants" always left Mom in tatters. Later on, Dad would just leave the room and go out to his work shed and sit and rock and rock in that old chair of his.

People probably thought we were deficient in brain power to be taken in by such cheap tricks. But just try putting yourself in our shoes. He was the only son, the only brother, the oldest child. He was intelligent and fun, and knew how to coax laughter out of a stone. He was surrounded by a bevy of admirers; everywhere he went, he trailed friends. He was athletic, won races, amassed trophies. He got lead parts in school plays. He won class elections. And he was beautiful. His face was rugged and laughing; his body was muscular and golden, even in January. He moved with the grace of a tiger. He dazzled. He shone.

By the time I was thirteen, Zackary's halo was dimming, but I still adored him. He was twenty-four years old, still living at home, still guzzling chocolate cakes, still borrowing the car. He needed money for his girlfriends and his liquor and his poker, and home was a cheap place to live. Cranky and delightful, moody and captivating, he still played the hero's role in our house.

Then Lizzie got sick. She wasn't just sick. She had leukemia,[4] and every one of us knew she was going to die. She was the youngest, the quiet one, the gentle one. She idolized Zack even more than the rest of us, because she was only seven, too young to see any of his flaws. He was her knight in shining armor, and she was forever looking for him to ride by her hospital room. "Why doesn't Zack come?" she kept asking. Once, just once, he arrived with a comic book for her, and her white little face lit up so brightly that you could almost convince yourself she might get better. He even made her laugh, and all our hearts went out to him in gratitude. But apart from that, he never once visited her during those last awful six weeks in the hospital. He was on drinking rampages day after day, or else he'd sober up enough to spend a week trying to win liquor money at the poker table.

One day Mom had the courage to plead, "Please, Zackary. Go see Lizzie. She keeps asking for you. *Please.*"

He sat down and put his head in his hands, saying, "I'm in terrible pain, Mom. I'm so frustrated. I can't help her." To which she replied, stiffly, "You can. You can visit her."

4 **leukemia:** a sometimes fatal disease caused by an abnormal number of white blood cells

Then he rose from his chair and threw a book on the floor. "Quit nagging!" he snapped at her. "I'm too old for that. I can handle my own life. I don't need you telling me what to do."

Zack lost a job and got another, and then lost that one, too. He was forever taking off in the family car, just as we were needing it to go to the hospital. But Mom forgave him for everything. "He's sensitive," she'd say. "He's taking it hard, and he can't face what's ahead for us. This is his way of coping. He's probably suffering more than the rest of us." Suffering, my foot, I thought.

That last day, the day that Lizzie died, we were all at the hospital to watch it happen—all, of course, except Zackary. Then the nurse came in and said that no, she was not asleep, she was gone.

There she was, our Lizzie, tubes coming out of her all over, machines ticking away, and nothing left of her at all. I tasted the words, "Gone. Dead," and they had no meaning at all for me. The closest I could come to a definition was "Not there anymore," but this was too large a concept for me to absorb. I could understand only the rage and the grief.

When we all walked out into the corridor, there he was. Zackary. Sobered up, dressed in the outfit Lizzie loved best: the tight jeans and the Mickey Mouse shirt. He stood there grinning, his arms overflowing with gifts—a hot-pink teddy bear, a bundle of comics, a Barbie doll in a bride's dress, a bouquet of five orchids. *Hail, the conquering hero comes.* Orchids, I thought. *Orchids.* I fled to the hospital washroom and was sick into the basin.

Four days later, he came home. He'd been heaven-knows-where in the meantime. He had on a clean white shirt, open at the neck, and his jeans. It was summer, and his skin was shining, gleaming, tanned, so that you knew he'd been at the beach a lot—down the South Shore, maybe. He'd never looked more handsome. Scudding[5] across my mind came the thought: If you can't find a job, Zack, try Sears catalogue, Men's Clothing division. You're a photographer's dream.

He sat down, head in his hands, of course. Don't move, I silently begged my mother. *Don't move.* But she went over and sat down beside him, placing her hand on his back. Then the words came, but no tears. "I'm sorry. I'm sorry," and variations on the theme. Start the Prodigal Son bit, I thought, and I'll kill you. But he did. ". . . no longer worthy to be called thy son," he finished, his voice suitably uneven. "Make me as one

5 **scudding:** running swiftly

of thy hired servants." My mother was kissing his hand and crying. I had a terrible desire to spit. Thirteen years old and a girl, and it was all I could do to keep from standing up and spitting on the carpet beside his feet. My father did stand up.

"I agree one hundred percent," he said, his voice soft and even, although the tears continued to roll down his cheeks. I marveled that he could do this. If I were to try to speak while crying, I knew that my speech would be peppered with hiccups and sobs, that my mouth and face would be all distorted and screwed up. "About being unworthy, I mean," he went on. "Over the years, I been wondering what to do about forgiveness. The Bible is all the time saying we should forgive one another. Your mother seems to be able to do it real easy, but I find I'm no good at it at all anymore. Seems to me that even the good Lord Himself wouldn't have wanted us all to just lie down and be walked over."

Zackary was looking at the floor now, his hands clasped tight, eyes dry and moving to and fro, like they were memorizing the pattern on the carpet.

"You have two choices, my boy," said Dad, his words still firm and quiet. "You can stick around and be just what you suggest. You can be one of our hired servants. I should've taken you up on that proposal fourteen years back. You can bake cakes and clean floors and wash dishes and mow lawns and clean all your junk out of the garage. You can paint the house. You can iron your own shirts. You can spread your charm around on a daily basis, instead of saving it up for special occasions."

There was a long silence. I think my dad was breathing hard, or doing whatever it took to get himself under control. Then he started to speak again.

"I hate to bring any more misery into this house than we already have, Zackary, but I'm giving you another choice." He looked hard at Zack, and then he shouted, so that we all jumped, *"Look at me, Zackary!"*

Zackary looked. He looked up from under his lids, and I thought, He looks shifty. He doesn't even look handsome to me anymore. Cheap, I thought. Cheap and shifty.

"If you don't like the first choice," said my dad, his voice quiet again, "there's always the second. You can clear out."

Nothing happened for maybe as long as five minutes, and Zack was staring at the carpet again, eyes darting. Nobody spoke. You could hear Mom sniffling, and from time to time a chain saw somewhere down the street whined, but mostly the silence was just pressing in on our ears. I sat there counting the flowers on the wallpaper so that I wouldn't be able to look at him.

Then Zackary rose and went upstairs to his room. We could hear him moving around up there, shuffling about, opening drawers, thunking things down. In about half an hour, he came down the stairs carrying two suitcases. He stopped at the bottom, and then came over and touched Mom on the shoulder. That's all. Then he just walked out the door without a word.

▲   ▲   ▲

I grieved a lot after Zack left. I grieved for Lizzie, of course, and I grieved for Mom and Dad, and I grieved for my own broken dream. Zack rode the rails out West, and we heard from Alberta friends that he drifted around the small towns out there, trying this job and that, playing poker, drinking cheap wine, always moving on.

I think Mom saw the justice of what Dad did, but I don't think she ever forgave him, either. She lost two children in one week, and that's too many for someone who had only four to begin with. She became senile early—in her late sixties—and she used to sit all day in a chair in the nursing home's common room, with her head drooped over on one side. Her hair was straight and ragged, her eyes open but empty. Her hands would be clasped in front of her, knuckles white, and she'd be forever and ever muttering, "All my fault. All my fault." Or occasionally she'd yell, in a loud tormented voice, "Too late! Too late!" Then the nurses would come running and give her a sedative.

▲   ▲   ▲

I'm married now, with three children, and I hardly ever think about Zackary anymore. I'm too busy with my own life and my own family. My children are all girls, two of them quiet and sweet, but the third like quicksilver, pretty and mischievous, quick-tempered and full of laughter. Our home revolves around the magic of her personality. She sheds light upon all of us. Her name is Stephanie, and she is thirteen years old. The other day she became angry at something one of her friends had done. Racing into our kitchen, she pushed her two sisters aside, and, seizing a jug of milk from the table, hurled it at the opposite wall. There was a loud crash, and crockery and milk flew in all directions. Then Stephanie sat down on a chair, with her head in her hands. Finally she lifted up her beautiful little face, framed by her long golden hair, and looked up at me from under a fringe of curling lashes.

"Mom, darling," she began, voice faltering, "I'm so sorry. I'm so, so, so sorry. I've gone and done it again." She rose from the chair with a familiar grace, and passed her hand across her forehead, sighing. "I can't imagine what came over me. Mom, sweetie. Can you forgive me? I could die with being sorry. Tell me what I can do to make me feel good again. I feel so terrible. I can hardly bear it."

I looked at her, listened to her, and longed to hold her in my arms and whisper consolation. But somewhere in the back of my head, I could hear a voice shouting, "Too late! Too late!"

I looked at Stephanie again. Despite her agonized expression, her eyes were dry. I recalled that these temper tantrums had been pretty frequent of late, as had the moving speeches of regret and apology. I had put it all down to the shifting hormones of a thirteen-year-old, and assumed that the violence would eventually pass. I looked now at the wall. The pitcher had cracked the paint where it had hit, and there was milk from one side of the room to the other. The floor was a lake, and drops of sticky milk were clinging to windows, curtains, kitchen utensils, dishes.

Something else. My two other daughters were watching this drama from the doorway. They were looking at Stephanie and they were studying me. I did not like the look on their faces.

"Stephanie," I began, keeping my voice friendly, "if you want to do something to feel better, I'll help you." She smiled a grateful smile. "I'm going over to Mrs. Vincent's," I continued, "to help her hang her new living room curtains. While I'm gone, I want you to clean up the milk and the broken china. There are rags and a pail at the bottom of the basement stairs. The curtains will have to be washed by hand, because the red dye runs. They're cotton, so you'll have to iron them. You'll also find milk on all those utensils in their container, as well as on most surfaces. Those china jugs are on sale at Zeller's, and I'd like you to take that allowance money you've been saving and go downtown for a new one. We have some green paint left over from when we painted the kitchen, so fortunately you won't have to buy that. You can repaint that wall on Saturday morning. I'll see that no one gets in your way."

Then, lest I weaken at the sight of her stricken face, I tiptoed through the milk and walked out of the kitchen.

"Thank you, Zackary," I said.

"*What?*" she said.

"Nothing important," I lied, and shut the door behind me. ∽

Keeping Hair

RAMONA WILSON

My grandmother had braids
at the thickest, pencil wide
held with bright wool
cut from her bed shawl.
No teeth left but white hair
combed and wet carefully
early each morning.
The small wild plants found among stones
on the windy and brown plateaus
revealed their secrets to her hand
and yielded to her cooking pots.
She made a sweet amber water
from willows,
boiling the life out
to pour onto her old head.
"It will keep your hair."
She bathed my head once
rain water not sweeter.
The thought that once
when I was so very young
her work-bent hands
very gently and smoothly
washed my hair in willows
may also keep my heart.

GIRL ARRANGING HER HAIR
1885–86
Mary Cassatt

Lectures on How You Never Lived Back Home

M. Evelina Galang

You grew up hearing two languages—one you can pull apart, name, slap a series of rules to, twist like clay-dough in a child's hand—the other you cannot explain, you listen and you know. It is a language you understand intuitively—like being able to read the sunrise, the strips of pink and orange, the clumps of uneven clouds, a thin patch of grey and the moon and somehow, without thinking twice, you know what kind of day it will be. You understand like this because you are the first born. First generation. First American. First cousin. First hope.

Back home, one of your grandmothers sewed children's clothing by hand and sold them in an open-air market. The other grandmother raised seven children on her own, gathering them up, hiding them away in the provinces along the sea, away from Japanese soldiers, away from American fighters. Away from war. Your grandmother feared the safety of all her children, especially her young ladies. Your mother survived wartime. She was smart and well-read and ambitious, skipped grades, travelled across the oceans, met your father in Milwaukee, gave up her princess status to be your mother. As a boy, your dad farmed fish out of monsoon-swollen rice paddies, cut school to hitchhike from Pampanga to Rizal[1] just to see MacArthur.[2]

---

1 **Pampanga to Rizal:** Philippine provinces, one north of Manila Bay and one southeast of the bay

2 **MacArthur:** famous American World War II general

Somewhere in his youth, he spied on American GIs and caught on to this notion of democracy, this notion of rights. His rights, his family's rights, the rights of his countrymen. The rights taken first by three hundred years of Spanish rule, then Japanese terror and war, then of course, there were the Americans and their intentions. After sneaking about soldier camps, making friends with a GI from Atlanta, bumming cigarettes from another one from Pasadena, your father worked his way out of those provinces, studied hard at school. He passed his boards, passed immigration, slipped into that ballroom on Racine and Wisconsin, and charmed his way into your mother's life.

They raised you to understand that back home, a young girl serves her parents, lives to please them, fetches her father's slippers and her mother's cups of tea. Back home a young girl learns to embroider fine stitches, learns parlor dances, wears white uniforms at all-girl schools, convent schools. She never crosses her legs or wears skirts above the knee. Back home a girl does not date. She is courted. And when there is a young man present, there is always a chaperon. Young ladies grow up to be young housewives, good mothers, and in their old age, they still behave like obedient daughters.

You, on the other hand, have never had to obey a curfew because of war, never had to tiptoe through your own house, never had to read your books underneath a blanket where no soldier would see. As far as you knew, your curfew was your curfew because Mom and Dad said so. You were raised in suburbia in a split-level house, always in fashion, even when you were only two, dressed in your white lace and pink ribbons, toting your very own parasol.[3] You've never been without heat, without food, without parents. All your life your worries consisted of boys and pimples and overdue books. You had your first boy-girl party when you were five years old, played Pin-the-Tail-on-the-Donkey and kissed Timmy Matasaki underneath the dining room table. You had a bad habit of talking back. You learned how to scream no to your parents, and it didn't matter if you were punished, slapped across the face, sent away to sulk, banished to the kitchen, you still opened your mouth and the words came out.

You grew up pouring chicken soy sauce dishes over beds of steamed rice, never mashing potatoes until you were on your own, eating your meals with a spoon in your right hand, a fork in the left, marvelling at

3 **parasol:** small umbrella, usually feminine-looking and colorful

the Americans and how they could balance entire meals on one fork, or the Chinese who could eat bowls of rice with two sticks. Your family roasted pigs on a spit, while next door, the neighbors cooked brats and burgers on electric grills.

From the start, you were a piece that did not fit, never given the chance to be like the rest—the ones with blond hair and red hair and something someone called strawberry. The ones with eyes that change like the ocean—green to blue to seafoam, depending on the color of their sweater. Your eyes have always been black. Your hair dark. Straight. No variety. To the kids at school, you were no different from the other Oriental girl, the one who spoke English with a chopped-up accent. To your aunts and uncles you were turning into a *bratty Americana*, loose like those blond children, mouthy like the kids who ran the streets wild. They worried you might grow up too indelicate for marriage.

Now you are well over twenty-five and still single. The old aunts raise one eyebrow and say, See? But you know, it's because you refuse to settle for less than best. Anyone can get married, you say. You not only tell men off, you ask them out. . . .

Your home is in Bucktown, Wicker Park, Ravenswood, Illinois, and because you won't admit the fact that what your parents call "back home" has made a place in your house, because you are not white, and still you are not one of them—the foreigners—you continue to displease everyone. Your father's headache is mostly just you. He has been known to throw his hands up, call you stubborn, say *Bahala na!* It's up to you. Your choice. Your responsibility.

Still, in the privacy of your kitchen, you admit you cannot live without your family, your history, this ideal called "your people." You cannot divorce yourself from yourself. You know you are the hyphen in American-born. Your identity scrawls the length and breadth of the page, American-born-girl. American-born-Filipina. Because you have always had one foot planted in the Midwest, one foot floating on the islands, and your arms have stretched across the generations, barely kissing your father's province, your children's future, the dreams your mother has for you. Because you were meant for the better life, whatever that is, been told you mustn't forget where you come from, what others have done for you. Because all your life you've simply been told.

Just told. Because a council of ancestors—including a few who are not yet dead, who are not even related to you—haunt you, you do your best. You try. You struggle. And somehow, when you stand in the center of a room, and the others look on, you find yourself acting out your role. Smart American girl, beautiful Filipina, dutiful daughter. ～

Birth-Order Blues

PAULA LYNN PARKS

Birth-order scientists have observed children and their roles within the family. The result has been some interesting theories of how personalities develop.

THE ONLY CHILD Picture children lined up at noon with their lunch boxes in hand. "See the kid with the attaché case? That's the only child," says Kevin Leman, a psychologist in Tucson and author of *The Birth Order Book*. "From ages 5, 6 and 7, they are much like little adults," Leman says. With what often is so much adult attention and so many expectations, it's no wonder "onlies" tend to surpass their peers in intellectual and emotional development. The downside of such indulgence is they may be less willing to share their toys.

THE ELDEST CHILD Along with being expected to meet high parental standards, the eldest child is often asked to blaze the trail for younger siblings. Not surprisingly, the eldest child tends to follow his parents' example, and he appreciates order, rules and structure. And a family can have *two* firstborns—the first daughter and the first son. Either way, that child tends to be responsible and comfortable being in charge. The downside? Particularly in siblings' eyes, the eldest child can be viewed as bossy.

THE MIDDLE CHILD Children born between the first and the last child probably have the worst reputation: weirdo or troublemaker. Middle children don't *want* to be bad; they just want to be a little different. So if the eldest is an athlete, the second-born may seek glory in the arts. This desire to be different is often seen in same-gender siblings.

"Nobody is excited about the same ol' thing over and over," explains Sandra E. Cox, Ph.D., a psychologist in Los Angeles who did her dissertation on the middle youngster in a three-child family. "So the middle child goes out there and acts different, looks different and does things differently; then people pay attention to her." One good thing about middle children, however, is that because they sometimes get pulled into the real-life dramas involving elder and younger siblings, middle-borns are natural mediators and negotiators.

THE YOUNGEST CHILD Completely comfortable with being the center of attention, the baby of the family is usually friendly and outgoing; he never meets a stranger. But he can also be manipulative and let his siblings take the fall for him. Because the youngest is considered cute and helpless one minute, then teased for not keeping up the next, he often tries to prove to the world that he should be taken seriously.

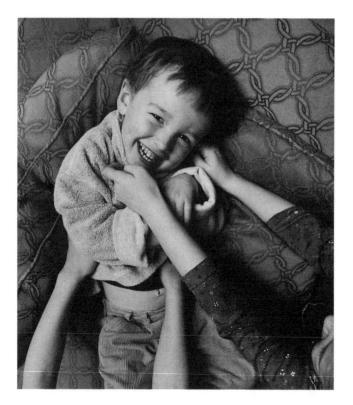

BEYOND THE BIRTH-ORDER BOX All this may sound as if children are walking stereotypes and slaves to their birth order, but nothing could be further from the truth. "Children learn to do certain things in certain roles by what their parents encourage," explains Karen Fraser Wyche, Ph.D., a clinical psychologist and Brown University professor.

For instance, if Mom is still making lunch for the 16-year-old "baby" of the family and is still calling him "pumpkin," that's his cue that he doesn't have to be responsible. Meanwhile, at the same age, the eldest may have heard: "I don't care *what* I do for your brother and sister; I expect more from you." ❧

Third Child

ERMA BOMBECK

Someone, who has wisely remained anonymous, once said that children are like waffles. The first one should be used to season the grill and then tossed out.

Studies made on first children say they're not all that bad. They are usually shy, serious and sensitive, are academically superior, and are more likely to be an Einstein.

Second children, on the other hand, are relaxed, independent, cheerful, lean toward creativity and are more likely to be a Picasso.

No one has had the courage to find—let alone study—child No. 3 and the ones who follow, whom I call et ceteras.[1]

Is there life after the first two children? What are the et ceteras like?

I have discovered the third child has a few attributes of his own. He has itchy feet and joins other families for three or four months, often without being noticed. He is not intimidated by anyone, has a great sense of humor and is apt to be a game show host.

Part of their uniqueness is that third children have no history. There are no footprints of them in the baby book, no record of their baptism, no snapshots of their birthdays and no report cards to show they ever were.

---

1 **et ceteras:** from Latin, meaning "and so forth," or others of the same kind

Their childhood diseases are uneventful, their first words fall on deaf ears, and toilet training is a lonely affair with no one to applaud their efforts.

The third child learns early that he is odd man out and has broken the family symmetry.

Kitchen chairs come four to a set, breakfast rolls four to a package and milk four cups to a quart. Rides at Disneyland accommodate two to a seat, the family car carries four comfortably, and beds come in twos, not threes.

The third child is the one who gets called the other two's names before the mother finally remembers his. He goes through a lifetime of comparisons: "You're not going to be as tall as your brother. . .as smart as your sister. . .as athletic as your father."

I personally feel there's a lot to be said for the et cetera children, who get a fast family shuffle and who thrive on neglect and somehow appear one day all grown up.

They not only know who they are and what they are, but they've dealt very early with the two things that most children fear the most: competition and loneliness. ∽

Growing Up

GARY SOTO

Now that Maria was a tenth-grader, she felt she was too grown-up to have to go on family vacations. Last year, the family had driven three hundred miles to see their uncle in West Covina.[1] There was nothing to do. The days were hot, with a yellow sky thick with smog they could feel on their fingertips. They played cards and watched game shows on television. After the first four days of doing nothing while the grown-ups sat around talking, the kids finally got to go to Disneyland.

Disneyland stood tall with castles and bright flags. The Matterhorn had wild dips and curves that took your breath away if you closed your eyes and screamed. The Pirates of the Caribbean didn't scare anyone but was fun anyway, and so were the teacups and It's a Small World. The parents spoiled the kids, giving each of them five dollars to spend on trinkets. Maria's younger sister, Irma, bought a Pinocchio coloring book and a candy bracelet. Her brothers, Rudy and John, spent their money on candy that made their teeth blue.

Maria saved her money. She knew everything was overpriced, like the Mickey Mouse balloons you could get for a fraction of the price in Fresno. Of course, the balloon at Hanoian's supermarket didn't have a Mickey Mouse face, but it would bounce and float and eventually pop like any other balloon.

Maria folded her five dollars, tucked it in her red purse, and went on rides until she got sick. After that, she sat on a bench, jealously watching other teenage girls who seemed much better dressed than she was. She felt stricken by poverty. All the screaming kids in nice clothes probably

1 **West Covina:** city near Los Angeles, California

came from homes with swimming pools in their backyards, she thought. Yes, her father was a foreman at the paper mill, and yes, she had a Dough-boy swimming pool in her backyard, but *still*, things were not the same. She had felt poor, and her sundress, which seemed snappy in Fresno, was out of style at Disneyland, where every other kid was wearing Esprit shirts and Guess jeans.

This year Maria's family planned to visit an uncle in San Jose.[2] Her father promised to take them to Great America, but she knew that the grown-ups would sit around talking for days before they remembered the kids and finally got up and did something. They would have to wait until the last day before they could go to Great America. It wasn't worth the boredom.

"Dad, I'm not going this year," Maria said to her father. He sat at the table with the newspaper in front of him.

"What do you mean?" he asked, slowly looking up. He thought a moment and said, "When I was a kid we didn't have the money for vacations. I would have been happy to go with my father."

"I know, I know. You've said that a hundred times," she snapped.

"What did you say?" he asked, pushing his newspaper aside.

Everything went quiet. Maria could hear the hum of the refrigerator and her brothers out in the front yard arguing over a popsicle stick, and her mother in the backyard watering the strip of grass that ran along the patio.

Her father's eyes locked on her with a dark stare. Maria had seen that stare before. She pleaded in a soft daughterly voice, "We never do anything. It's boring. Don't you understand?"

"No, I don't understand. I work all year, and if I want to go on a vacation, then I go. And my family goes too." He took a swallow of ice water, and glared.

"You have it too easy," he continued. "In Chihuahua,[3] my town, we worked hard. You worked, even *los chavalos!*[4] And you showed respect to your parents, something you haven't learned."

Here it comes, Maria thought, stories about his childhood in Mexico. She wanted to stuff her ears with wads of newspaper to keep from hearing him. She could recite his stories word-for-word. She couldn't wait until she was in college and away from them.

---

2 **San Jose:** city southeast of San Francisco, California

3 **Chihuahua:** city in northern Mexico

4 *los chavalos:* the young people

"Do you know my father worked in the mines? That he nearly lost his life? And today his lungs are bad." He pounded his chest with hard, dirt-creased knuckles.

Maria pushed back her hair and looked out the window at her brothers running around in the front yard. She couldn't stand it anymore. She got up and walked away, and when he yelled for her to come back, she ignored him. She locked herself in her bedroom and tried to read *Seventeen*, though she could hear her father complaining to her mother, who had come in when she had heard the yelling.

"Habla, con tu mocosa,"[5] she heard him say.

She heard the refrigerator door open. He was probably getting a beer, a "cold one," as he would say. She flipped through the pages of her magazine and stopped at a Levi's ad of a girl about her age walking between two happy-looking guys on a beach. She wished she were that girl, that she had another life. She turned the page and thought, I bet you he gets drunk and drives crazy tomorrow.

Maria's mother was putting away a pitcher of Kool-Aid the boys had left out. She looked at her husband, who was fumbling with a wadded-up napkin. His eyes were dark, and his thoughts were on Mexico, where a father was respected and his word, right or wrong, was final. "Rafael, she's growing up; she's a teenager. She talks like that, but she still loves you."

"Sure, and that's how she shows her love, by talking back to her father." He rubbed the back of his neck and turned his head trying to make the stiffness go away. He knew it was true, but he was the man of the house and no daughter of his was going to tell him what to do.

Instead, it was his wife, Eva, who told him what to do. "Let the girl stay. She's big now. She don't want to go on rides no more. She can stay with her *nina*."[6]

The father drank his beer and argued, but eventually agreed to let his daughter stay.

The family rose just after six the next day and was ready to go by seven-thirty. Maria stayed in her room. She wanted to apologize to her father but couldn't. She knew that if she said, "Dad, I'm sorry," she would break into tears. Her father wanted to come into her room and say, "We'll do something really special this vacation. Come with us, honey."

5 *Habla, con tu mocosa*: Talk to your snotty girl

6 *nina*: godmother

But it was hard for him to show his emotions around his children, especially when he tried to make up to them.

The mother kissed Maria. "Maria, I want you to clean the house and then walk over to your *nina's*. I want no monkey business while we're gone, do you hear me?"

"*Sí*, Mama."

"Here's the key. You water the plants inside and turn on the sprinkler every couple of days." She handed Maria the key and hugged her. "You be good. Now, come say goodbye to your father."

Reluctantly, she walked out in her robe to the front yard and, looking down at the ground, said goodbye to her father. The father looked down and said goodbye to the garden hose at his feet.

After they left, Maria lounged in her pajamas listening to the radio and thumbing through magazines. Then she got up, fixed herself a bowl of Cocoa Puffs, and watched "American Bandstand." Her dream was to dance on the show, to look at the camera, smile, and let everyone in Fresno see that she could have a good time, too.

But an ill feeling stirred inside her. She felt awful about arguing with her father. She felt bad for her mother and two brothers, who would have to spend the next three hours in the car with him. Maybe he would do something crazy, like crash the car on purpose to get back at her, or fall asleep and run the car into an irrigation ditch. And it would be her fault.

She turned the radio to a news station. She listened for half an hour, but most of the news was about warships in the Persian Gulf and a tornado in Texas. There was no mention of her family.

Maria began to calm down because, after all, her father was really nice beneath his gruffness. She dressed slowly, made some swishes with the broom in the kitchen, and let the hose run in a flower bed while she painted her toenails with her mother's polish. Afterward, she called her friend Becky to tell her that her parents had let her stay home, that she was free—for five days at least.

"Great," Becky said. "I wish my mom and dad would go away and let me stay by myself."

"No, I have to stay with my godmother." She made a mental note to give her *nina* a call. "Becky, let's go to the mall and check out the boys."

"All right."

"I'll be over pretty soon."

Maria called her *nina*, who said it was OK for her to go shopping, but to be at her house for dinnertime by six. After hanging up, Maria took off her jeans and T-shirt, and changed into a dress. She went through her mother's closet to borrow a pair of shoes and drenched her wrists in Charlie perfume. She put on coral-pink lipstick and a smudge of blue eyeshadow. She felt beautiful, although a little self-conscious. She took off some of the lipstick and ran water over her wrists to dilute the fragrance.

While she walked the four blocks to Becky's house, she beamed happiness until she passed a man who was on his knees pulling weeds from his flower bed. At his side, a radio was reporting a traffic accident. A big rig had overturned after hitting a car near Salinas, twenty miles from San Jose.

A wave of fear ran through her. Maybe it was *them*. Her smile disappeared, and her shoulders slouched. No, it couldn't be, she thought. Salinas is not that close to San Jose. Then again, maybe her father wanted to travel through Salinas because it was a pretty valley with wide plains and oak trees, and horses and cows that stared as you passed them in your speeding car. But maybe it did happen; maybe they had gotten in an awful wreck.

By the time she got to Becky's house, she was riddled with guilt, since it was she who would have disturbed her father and made him crash.

"Hi," she said to Becky, trying to look cheerful.

"You look terrific, Maria," Becky said. "Mom, look at Maria. Come inside for a bit."

Maria blushed when Becky's mother said she looked gorgeous. She didn't know what to do except stare at the carpet and say, "Thank you, Mrs. Ledesma."

Becky's mother gave them a ride to the mall, but they'd have to take a bus back. The girls first went to Macy's, where they hunted for a sweater, something flashy but not too flashy. Then they left to have a Coke and sit by the fountain under an artificial tree. They watched people walk by, especially the boys, who, they agreed, were dumb but cute nevertheless.

They went to The Gap, where they tried on some skirts, and ventured into The Limited, where they walked up and down the aisles breathing in the rich smells of 100-percent wool and silk. They were about to leave, when Maria heard once again on someone's portable radio that a family had been killed in an auto accident near Salinas. Maria stopped smiling for a moment as she pictured her family's overturned Malibu station wagon.

Becky sensed that something was wrong and asked, "How come you're so quiet?"

Maria forced a smile. "Oh, nothing. I was just thinking."

" 'bout what?"

Maria thought quickly. "Oh, I think I left the water on at home." This could have been true. Maria remembered pulling the hose from the flower bed, but couldn't remember if she had turned the water off.

Afterward they rode the bus home with nothing to show for their three hours of shopping except a small bag of See's candies. But it had been a good day. Two boys had followed them, joking and flirting, and they had flirted back. The girls gave them made-up telephone numbers, then turned away and laughed into their hands.

"They're fools," Becky said, "but cute."

Maria left Becky when they got off the bus, and started off to her *nina*'s house. Then she remembered that the garden hose might still be running at home. She hurried home, clip-clopping clumsily in her mother's shoes.

The garden hose was rolled neatly against the trellis. Maria decided to check the mail and went inside. When she pushed open the door, the living room gave off a quietness she had never heard before. Usually the TV was on, her younger brothers and sister were playing, and her mother could be heard in the kitchen. When the telephone rang, Maria jumped. She kicked off her shoes, ran to the phone, and picked up the receiver only to hear a distant clicking sound.

"Hello, hello?" Maria's heart began to thump. Her mind went wild with possibilities. An accident, she thought, they're in an accident, and it's all my fault. "Who is it? Dad? Mom?"

She hung up and looked around the room. The clock on the television set glowed 5:15. She gathered the mail, changed into jeans, and left for her *nina*'s house with a shopping bag containing her nightie and a toothbrush.

Her *nina* was happy to see her. She took Maria's head in her hands and gave it a loud kiss.

"Dinner is almost ready," she said, gently pulling her inside.

"Oh, good. Becky and I only had popcorn for lunch."

They had a quiet evening together. After dinner, they sat on the porch watching the stars. Maria wanted to ask her *nina* if she had heard from her parents. She wanted to know if the police had called to report that they had gotten into an accident. But she just sat on the porch swing, letting anxiety eat a hole in her soul.

The family was gone for four days. Maria prayed for them, prayed that she would not wake up to a phone call saying that their car had been found in a ditch. She made a list of the ways she could be nicer to them: doing the dishes without being asked, watering the lawn, hugging her father after work, and playing with her youngest brother, even if it bored her to tears.

At night Maria worried herself sick listening to the radio for news of an accident. She thought of her uncle Shorty and how he fell asleep and crashed his car in the small town of Mendota. He lived confined to a motorized wheelchair and was scarred with burns on the left side of his face.

"Oh, please, don't let anything like that happen to them," she prayed.

In the morning she could barely look at the newspaper. She feared that if she unfolded it, the front page would feature a story about a family from Fresno who had flown off the roller coaster at Great America. Or that a shark had attacked them as they bobbed happily among the white-tipped waves. Something awful is going to happen, she said to herself as she poured Rice Krispies into a bowl.

But nothing happened. Her family returned home, dark from lying on the beach and full of great stories about the Santa Cruz boardwalk and Great America and an Egyptian museum. They had done more this year than in all their previous vacations.

"Oh, we had fun," her mother said, pounding sand from her shoes before entering the house.

Her father gave her a tight hug as her brothers ran by, dark from hours of swimming.

Maria stared at the floor, miffed. How dare they have so much fun? While she worried herself sick about them, they had splashed in the waves, stayed at Great America until nightfall, and eaten at all kinds of restaurants. They even went shopping for fall school clothes.

Feeling resentful as Johnny described a ride that dropped straight down and threw your stomach into your mouth, Maria turned away and went off to her bedroom, where she kicked off her shoes and thumbed through an old *Seventeen*. Her family was alive and as obnoxious as ever. She took back all her promises. From now on she would keep to herself and ignore them. When they asked, "Maria, would you help me," she would pretend not to hear and walk away.

"They're heartless," she muttered. "Here I am worrying about them, and there they are having fun." She thought of the rides they had gone on, the hours of body surfing, the handsome boys she didn't get to see, the restaurants, and the museum. Her eyes filled with tears. For the first time in years, she hugged a doll, the one her grandmother Lupe had stitched together from rags and old clothes.

"Something's wrong with me," she cried softly. She turned on her radio and heard about a single-engined plane that had crashed in Cupertino, a city not far from San Jose. She thought of the plane and the people inside, how the pilot's family would suffer.

She hugged her doll. Something was happening to her, and it might be that she was growing up. When the news ended, and a song started playing, she got up and washed her face without looking in the mirror.

That night the family went out for Chinese food. Although her brothers fooled around, cracked jokes, and spilled a soda, she was happy. She ate a lot, and when her fortune cookie said, "You are mature and sensible," she had to agree. And her father and mother did too. The family drove home singing the words to "La Bamba" along with the car radio. ∾

RESPONDING TO CLUSTER THREE

HOW ARE WE INFLUENCED FAMILY?

Thinking Skill   COMPARING AND CONTRASTING

1. List three of Zack's irresponsible actions in "The Charmer." Zack's mother excuses him for these actions because she says he is "sensitive." Do you think this is a good excuse? Why or why not?

2. From "The Charmer," list one or two of Zack and Stephanie's actions. Then list how the family reacts to those actions. In a few sentences, **compare** how the two related family members are similar and **contrast** their differences. You may want to use a chart such as the one below.

Name	Individual Action	Family Reaction
Zack		
Stephanie		

3. A **metaphor** is a comparison between two things. For example, love is often compared to a rose. Explain what two things are being compared in "Keeping Hair."

4. In both "Lectures on How You Never Lived Back Home" and "Growing Up," the main characters (Ms. Galang and Maria) struggle with two desires: a desire to belong to the family and a desire to be independent from it. Find at least one quotation in one of the selections that shows how the character deals with these conflicting desires. In a short paragraph or discussion explain if you agree with the way the character resolves her struggle.

5. In your opinion, which family in Clusters One and Two exerts the most influence on its members? Why did you choose this family?

Writing Activity: Birth Order—Does It Describe You?

After reading "Birth-Order Blues" and "Third Child," **compare and contrast** your personality with the characteristics given for the birth order you hold in your family. Do these character traits apply to you? Explain.

A Strong Comparison/Contrast

• states the purpose for the comparison

• is organized in one of two ways:

   a) lists all similarities between two things, then lists all differences

   b) lists similarities and differences item by item

• summarizes the similarities and differences in the conclusion

CLUSTER THREE

How Do Families Deal with Problems?
Thinking Skill EVALUATING

Somebody's Son

RICHARD PINDELL

He sat, washed up on the side of the highway, a slim, sun-beaten drift-wood of a youth. He was hunched on his strapped-together suitcase, chin on hands, elbows on knees, staring down the road. Not a car was in sight. But for him, the dead, still Dakota plains were empty.

Now he was eager to write that letter he had kept putting off. Somehow, writing it would be almost like having company.

He unstrapped his suitcase and fished out of the pocket on the under-side of the lid a small, unopened package of stationery. Sitting down in the gravel of the roadside, he closed the suitcase and used it as a desk.

Dear Mom,

If Dad will permit it, I would like to come home. I know there's little chance he will. I'm not going to kid myself. I remember he said once, if I ever ran off, I might as well keep on going.

All I can say is that I felt leaving home was something I had to do. Before even considering college, I wanted to find out more about life and about me and the best way for us (life and me) to live with each other. Please tell Dad— and I guess this'll make him sore all over again—I'm still not certain that college is the answer for me. I think I'd like to work for a time and think it over.

You won't be able to reach me by mail, because I'm not sure where I'll be next. But in a few days I hope to be passing by our place. If there's any chance Dad will have me back, please ask him to tie a white cloth to the apple tree in the south pasture—you know the one, the Grimes Golden beside the tracks. I'll be going by on the train. If there's no cloth on the tree I'll just quietly, and with-out any hard feelings toward Dad—I mean that—keep on going.

Love, David

The sunset that evening was a violent one. Jagged clouds, trapped in cross-currents, rammed each other like primitive men-of-war[1] and burst into flames, burning one by one into deep purple ash.

It made the boy sad to see the sun go down. He had learned that always at the moment when darkness prevails, loneliness draws closer.

A series of headlights made a domino of the highway. High beams flickered over him curiously. He put out his thumb almost hesitantly, wishing he didn't have to emerge so suddenly, so menacingly. One by one, the cars passed him, their back draft slapping him softly, insultingly, on the cheek.

Much later, turning woodenly to gaze after a car, he saw the glow of tail-lights intensify. Brakes squealed. The car careened wildly to a stop, and he was running down the road to capture it, his breath rushing against his upturned collar and the taillights glowing nearer as in a dream.

A door was flung open like a friendly arm reaching out to a tired swimmer. "Hop in, boy."

It was a gruff, outdoors voice. "I pret' near missed you. You ain't easy to see out there."

"Thanks, mister."

"Forget it. Used the thumb a lot myself when I was a kid."

"How far are you going?" asked David.

The man named a small place in Iowa about two hundred miles away. David settled back in anticipation of a good ride.

"Where you headin'?" the man asked him.

David glanced at him. His nose was big and jutting; his mouth, wide and gentle. His was a face formed without beauty—and without hesitation. He had a tough-friendly way of accepting David as a man, something which David was still young enough to appreciate as a fine luxury.

The boy looked out on the highway with affection. It would be a good ride with a good companion. "Home," he said with a grin. "I'm heading home."

The man heard the smile in the boy's voice and chuckled. "That's a good feelin', ain't it? Where 'bouts?"

"Maryland. We have a farm about thirty miles outside of Baltimore."

"Where you been?"

"West Coast, Canada, a little of Mexico."

---

1 **men-of-war:** ancient soldiers

"And now you're hightailin' for home, huh?" There was a note in the man's voice as if this were a pattern he understood intimately.

"Yes, sir."

▲ ▲ ▲

David smiled wryly to himself, remembering another day. It was in the San Joaquin Valley.[2] He was picking grapes. As usual, the sun ruled mercilessly. Grape leaves drooped. Pickers were humped in varying attitudes of defense, some with bandannas covering the backs of their necks. Even the dirt had sagged beneath the blazing heat, crumbling into limp, heavy powder.

David looked down at his feet plowing through the grayish stuff. For four hours now it seemed he had not raised his eyes from his feet. He stopped abruptly and looked back down the row, measuring his progress. He had gone maybe fifty yards.

The faint clink of scissors landing in his half-filled basket came to him and then the foreman was bawling at him, "Hey! Where do you think you're going? It ain't lunchtime yet!" David stared at his feet and the dust; and his feet were stretching out as far as they could reach, his fist was tight around the handle of his suitcase, and the dust swirling madly behind him. He didn't even stop to pick up his money.

When he reached the highway and the cars kept passing him, it was all he could do to keep from jumping out in front of them to make them stop.

"Yeah," the driver was saying now, "I know how it is." The corners of his eyes crinkled as if he were going to smile, but he didn't. "I was out on that same old road when I was a kid. Bummin' around. Lettin' no grass grow under me. Sometimes wishin' it would."

"And then, afterward," David asked, "did you go back home?"

"Nope. I didn't have no home to go back to, like you do. The road was my only home. Lost my ma and pa when I was a little shaver. Killed in a car wreck."

"That's rough," David said with such feeling the man glanced at him sharply.

The boy was staring into the night. The man shifted his grip on the wheel, deftly straddling a dead jack rabbit. He spoke softly to the boy as if he were aware he was interrupting important thoughts. "Bet you could do with some sleep."

2 **San Joaquin Valley:** an agricultural region in California

"You sure you won't be needing me later to help keep you awake?" David asked.

"Don't worry 'bout me none. I like drivin' at night. You just lean back there and help yourself."

"Well, okay," David said. "Thanks."

Sometime later, he was awakened by a sharp decrease in speed. They were entering a town. He sat up and jerked the letter out of his jacket pocket. He had almost forgotten.

"Excuse me, sir, but would you mind stopping at a mailbox so I can mail this? I want to make sure that it gets home before I do."

"Course not," the man said. "Here's one comin' up now." He pulled over to the curb and stopped.

When the boy got back in, the man smiled kindly. "Bet your folks'll be tickled to hear from you."

"I hope so, sir." David tilted his head back and closed his eyes.

The next day, rides were slow. They were what David called "farmer rides," a few miles here, a couple of miles there, with long waits in between.

Toward nightfall, he forsook the unfriendly asphalt and swung onto a panting, slow-moving freight aimed stolidly east. As the train trundled laboriously over the Mississippi, a few drops of rain slapped the metal floor of his gondola car, and then, suddenly, he was surrounded by water, the river beneath him, and everywhere else, walls of rain. He crawled into a corner and huddled under some scraps of heavy paper that had been used to wrap freight.

For thirty miles, the rain pounded him, slashing his paper hut to tatters and turning his clothes into puddles of mush.

As, cold and wet, he swayed with the motion of the car, his last seven months haunted him. A spinning constellation of faces, flaring up and dying away, careened toward him. Faces of truck drivers, waitresses, salesmen, cops, employment agents, winos, tramps, cowboys, bartenders. Faces of people who had been kind to him; faces of people who had used him. They went on and on.

Well, he would never see them again. He had experienced them quickly, dazedly, as they had experienced him. He had no idea where they were now, and they did not know where he was.

Finally the rain stopped. He lunged erect, inviting the warm, night air to dry him. He looked out over the top of his racketing steel box. He faced east—toward home. *They* didn't have any idea where he was, either.

The train was hammering along beside a highway. He stared at the houses on the other side. How would it be at home? Would his house be like that one, the one with the porch light burning? Or would it be like that one, where the porch was dark and where over each of the lighted windows a yellow shade was pulled down firmly to the sill?

A couple of days later, in the middle of Maryland, maddeningly close to home, the flow of rides narrowed to a trickle and then ceased altogether. When cars weren't in sight, he walked. After a while, he didn't even bother to stop and hold out his thumb. Furiously, he walked.

Later, seated on the passenger train—the only freights around here ran at night—he wished with slow, frightened heartbeats that he were back on the road, headed the other way.

Three inches from his nose was the dust-stained window through which in a few minutes he would look out across his father's fields. Two different pictures tortured him—the tree with the white cloth and the tree without it. His throat closed and he could hardly breathe.

He tried to fortify himself with the idea that whether or not he still was welcome, at least he would see the place again.

The field was sliding closer, one familiar landmark at a time. He couldn't stop the train. The frenzied wheels were stamping out the end of the crescendo that had begun with the clink of the scissors in his half-filled basket of grapes. Nothing could postpone the denouement[3] now. The tree was around the next bend.

He couldn't look. He was too afraid the cloth would not be there—too afraid he would find, staring back at him, just another tree, just another field, just another somebody else's strange place, the way it always is on the long, long road, the nameless staring back at the nameless. He jerked away from the window.

Desperately, he nudged the passenger beside him. "Mister, will you do me a favor? Around this bend on the right, you'll see an apple tree. I wonder if you'll tell me if you see a white cloth tied to one of its branches?"

As they passed the field, the boy stared straight ahead. "Is it there?" he asked with an uncontrollable quaver.

"Son," the man said in a voice slow with wonder. "I see a white cloth tied on almost every twig." ❧

---

3 **denouement:** the final outcome

After the Divorce

JEWEL KILCHER

After the divorce
we moved to Homer
to live in a one bedroom apartment
behind Uncle Otto's machine shop.

My brothers slept in the water closet
after my dad painted it any color
they wanted. The pipes looked like
silver trees sprouting up through
the frames of their bunk beds.

For me, we took the door
off the coat closet
and built a narrow bed
four feet off the ground
with a ladder of rough wood
to climb up that hurt my bare feet.
My dad tried hard
to keep us all together
and work at the same time,
but things just weren't the same.
He pulled my hair when he brushed it
and didn't sing to us at night
before we went to sleep.

I was eight and started cooking.
Shane grocery shopped
and Atz, well, he was a kid.
By 7 A.M. every morning
we walked ourselves out to the road
and waited for the school bus
with all the other kids.
Looking for signs
of when life might strike random again
and scatter us like seeds
on the unknowable winds
of chance.

Gillian, Age Thirteen

AS TOLD TO JILL KREMENTZ

I was about four when my parents got divorced, and I don't remember anything that happened that year. It's like a total blank. I remember things that happened to me before then and afterwards, but it's like I have amnesia around the time they split up. No one believes me, but I do remember lots of things that happened to me *before* the divorce— from when I was really little. I can remember living in Holland when I was one, and I vividly remember parts of our house—like my brother's room and our stairway. We moved to Germany when I was two, and I remember even more about the year we spent there—things like going through my sister's toy chest and riding around the living room on my tricycle while my family clapped. The memories of those first three years are so important and precious to me that I guess I've always wanted to hold on to them. I hope I'll never forget them. Those are the years that Mommy and Daddy were still married.

From the time my parents got divorced until I was eleven, which is when my father got remarried, I always had the same wish whenever I blew out the candles on my birthday cake. I always wished that my parents would get back together again. For a long time I worried that I had actually caused the breakup, because whenever I did anything my older sister didn't like, she'd tell me that *I* was the reason my parents got divorced, that it was all my fault and if I hadn't been born they'd still be together. I'd cry and cry, but I'd never ask Mom or Dad if it was true— not because I subconsciously might have thought my sister was right, but mainly because I never really faced their divorce head-on. I just hung on to the notion that they'd get back together again.

One of the most painful consequences of the divorce for me has been that it's been hard to have an easygoing relationship with my mother. After Daddy moved out, I think she expected more of me—you know, being a perfect daughter and getting good report cards all the time. And it made her worry about money all the time, too. I always felt as though I was caught in the middle, and I resented that. Mommy would say things like "If you want to go to gymnastics class, you'll have to ask your father to pay for it," and Daddy would say, "You shouldn't be in the middle of this. If your mother wants me to pay for something, then she should call me." But of course he was making me the middleman, too, because I'd have to relay his message to her. Whenever I talked to either parent, it was like being on the telephone with someone who really wants to be speaking to someone else. If parents are going to get divorced in the first place, they should expect to pay the consequences, which include talking directly to each other—even if they hate each other. The kids shouldn't be dragged into their problems.

And I had enough problems just shuttling back and forth between two very different households. I hated going back and forth between my father's house and my mother's house, and I often asked myself—and them—why they couldn't live together again. It wasn't until after Dad married Meg that it dawned on me that if my parents had gotten remarried to each other they would have been miserable, which wouldn't have made my life very happy either!

Dad and Meg have a new baby, Jocelyn, whom I love very much. But I have to admit I'm envious of her—not jealous, but envious that she gets

to have a full-time Daddy. She's really lucky that every year of her life, until she goes away to college, her Daddy will be there—you know, when she learns to throw a ball or write her name. Whenever she does something for the first time, he'll be there. It makes me sad that Daddy hasn't been there for me full-time for the past ten years of my life.

A year ago my mother got remarried—to Bert—and it's been hard for me to adjust because we had to move into his apartment. I felt as if Mother had taken me out of my own home and put me into another place which she wanted me to think of as my home but which I really thought of as Bert's house. I only stayed there for a year, though, because I really wanted to live with Daddy and Meg, and so that's where I've been staying for this past year. It's much better for everybody, and I'm a lot happier. It's especially improved my relationship with Mommy—I spend every weekend with her—because now she's much more relaxed. Maybe it's because she doesn't feel so responsible for my actions—like if I don't do well on a test, she doesn't feel that it's *her* fault. We're much closer than we've ever been because we don't fight anymore.

My Bat Mitzvah[1] was nice because it gave me a chance to have some memories of an occasion with both my mother and father there. We even have a picture of all five of us, with me standing between Mommy and Daddy. The last time I remember them together is when I was three.

When parents divorce, I think everybody underestimates the child's mentality. Parents say things like "Oh, I know what's best for her—she doesn't really know," but it's not true. If a child wants to stay with his father or mother, there's a reason for it and parents should *listen* instead of doing all the talking.

I don't want to get married when I grow up because I don't want to get divorced. Not ever. You see, if I did marry I'd probably have a kid, and I wouldn't want to put somebody I loved in the position I'm in now. If you ask me, the real problem for anyone getting married these days is that divorce is such an easy out. I don't really know if I want to get married under conditions where if we have a fight or if my husband doesn't like the way I act around other people, all he has to do is ask me for a divorce. It's so stupid. I truly believe that most situations can be worked out—and ought to be. Divorce is like suicide. Instead of trying to solve their problems, people just kill their marriage because it's the easy way out.

---

1 **Bat Mitzvah:** Jewish ceremony for girls at age 13

It's still hard for me to say anything to my parents if something upsets me. Writing poetry has always been the best way for me to get my feelings out. That way, no one can get mad at me and things don't stay all bottled up inside of me, either. I have a big box with a lock on it where I keep all my writing. I've probably written over a hundred poems so far. These are a few of my favorites:

Why couldn't they stay together?
Like two dying stars—
Waiting till all was right to end it,
Waiting till I understood?
But no—
Like the sun and the moon
They split
Leaving me to be earth
Solid as they were not.

Like the Red Sea
Parted
Yet never joined again

Mommy's world
Daddy's world
So different

Sometimes I wonder
Which is better for me?
But I'll never really know.

I used to dream they'd marry again
They didn't
I used to dream everything was all right
It wasn't
I used to dream I was happy
I wasn't.

Getting the Facts of Life

PAULETTE CHILDRESS WHITE

The August morning was ripening into a day that promised to be a burner. By the time we'd walked three blocks, dark patches were showing beneath Momma's arms, and inside tennis shoes thick with white polish, my feet were wet against the cushions. I was beginning to regret how quickly I'd volunteered to go.

"Dog. My feet are getting mushy," I complained.

"You should've wore socks," Momma said, without looking my way or slowing down.

I frowned. In 1961 nobody wore socks with tennis shoes. It was bare legs, Bermuda shorts and a sleeveless blouse. Period.

Momma was chubby, but she could really walk. She walked the same way she washed clothes—up-and-down, up-and-down until she was done. She didn't believe in taking breaks.

This was my first time going to the welfare office with Momma. After breakfast, before we'd had time to scatter, she corralled everyone old enough to consider and announced in her serious-business voice that someone was going to the welfare office with her this morning. Cries went up.

Junior had his papers to do. Stella was going swimming at the high school. Dennis was already pulling the *Free Press* wagon across town every first Wednesday to get the surplus food—like that.

"You want clothes for school, don't you?" That landed. School opened in two weeks.

"I'll go," I said.

"Who's going to baby-sit if Minerva goes?" Momma asked.

Stella smiled and lifted her small golden nose. "I will," she said. "I'd rather baby-sit than do *that*."

That should have warned me. Anything that would make Stella offer to baby-sit had to be bad.

A small cheer probably went up among my younger brothers in the back rooms, where I was not too secretly known as "The Witch" because of the criminal licks I'd learned to give on my rise to power. I was twelve, third oldest under Junior and Stella, but I had long established myself as first in command among the kids. I was chief baby sitter, biscuit maker and broom wielder. Unlike Stella, who'd begun her development at ten, I still had my girl's body and wasn't anxious to have that changed. What would it mean but a loss of power? I liked things just the way they were. My interest in bras was even less than my interest in boys, and that was limited to keeping my brothers—who seemed destined for wildness—from taking over completely.

Even before we left, Stella had Little Stevie Wonder turned up on the radio in the living room, and suspicious jumping-bumping sounds were beginning in the back. They'll tear the house down, I thought, following Momma out the door.

We turned at Salliotte, the street that would take us straight up to Jefferson Avenue where the welfare office was. Momma's face was pinking in the heat, and I was huffing to keep up. From here, it was seven more blocks on the colored side, the railroad tracks, five blocks on the white side and there you were. We'd be cooked.

"Is the welfare office near the Harbor Show?" I asked. I knew the answer; I just wanted some talk.

"Across the street."

"Umm. Glad it's not way down Jefferson somewhere."

Nothing. Momma didn't talk much when she was outside. I knew that the reason she wanted one of us along when she had far to go was not for company but so she wouldn't have to walk by herself. I could understand that. To me, walking alone was like being naked or deformed —everyone seemed to look at you harder and longer. With Momma, the feeling was probably worse because you knew people were wondering if she were white, Indian maybe or really colored. Having one of us along, brown and clearly hers, probably helped define that. Still, it was like being a little parade, with Momma's pale skin and straight brown hair turning heads like the clang of cymbals. Especially on the colored side.

"Well," I said, "here we come to the bad part."

Momma gave a tiny laugh.

Most of Salliotte was a business street, with Old West-looking storefronts and some office places that never seemed to open. Ecorse,[1]

1 **Ecorse:** southwestern suburb of Detroit, Michigan

hinged onto southwest Detroit like a clothes closet, didn't seem to take itself seriously. There were lots of empty fields, some of which folks down the residential streets turned into vegetable gardens every summer. And there was this block where the Moonflower Hotel raised itself to three stories over the poolroom and Beaman's drugstore. Here, bad boys and drunks made their noise and did an occasional stabbing. Except for the cars that lined both sides of the block, only one side was busy—the other bordered a field of weeds. We walked on the safe side.

If you were a woman or a girl over twelve, walking this block—even on the safe side—could be painful. They usually hollered at you, and never mind what they said. Today, because it was hot and early, we made it by with only one weak "Hey baby" from a drunk sitting in the poolroom door.

"Hey baby yourself," I said, but not too loudly, pushing my flat chest out and stabbing my eyes in his direction.

"Minerva girl, you better watch your mouth with grown men like that," Momma said, her eyes catching me up in real warning, though I could see that she was holding down a smile.

"Well, he can't do nothing to me when I'm with you, can he?" I asked, striving to match the rise and fall of her black pumps.

She said nothing. She just walked on, churning away under a sun that clearly meant to melt us. From here to the tracks it was mostly gardens. It felt like the Dixie Peach I'd used to help water-wave my hair was sliding down with the sweat on my face, and my throat was tight with thirst. Boy, did I want a pop. I looked at the last little store before we crossed the tracks without bothering to ask.

Across the tracks, there were no stores and no gardens. It was shady, and the grass was June green. Perfect-looking houses sat in unfenced spaces far back from the street. We walked these five blocks without a word. We just looked and hurried to get through it. I was beginning to worry about the welfare office in earnest. A fool could see that in this part of Ecorse, things got serious.

We had been on welfare for almost a year. I didn't have any strong feelings about it—my life went on pretty much the same. It just meant watching the mail for a check instead of Daddy getting paid and occasional visits from a social worker that I'd always managed to miss. For Momma and whoever went with her, it meant this walk to the office and whatever went on there that made everyone hate to go. For Daddy, it seemed to bring the most change. For him, it meant staying away from home more than when he was working and a reason not to answer the phone.

At Jefferson, we turned left and there it was, halfway down the block. The Department of Social Services. I discovered some strong feelings. That fine name meant nothing. This was the welfare. The place for poor people. People who couldn't or wouldn't take care of themselves. Now I was going to face it, and suddenly I thought what I knew the others had thought, *What if I see someone I know?* I wanted to run back all those blocks to home.

I looked at Momma for comfort, but her face was closed and her mouth looked locked.

Inside, the place was gray. There were rows of long benches, like church pews, facing each other across a middle aisle that led to a central desk. Beyond the benches and the desk, four hallways led off to a maze of partitioned offices. In opposite corners, huge fans hung from the ceiling, humming from side to side, blowing the heavy air for a breeze.

Momma walked to the desk, answered some questions, was given a number and told to take a seat. I followed her through, trying not to see the waiting people—as though that would keep them from seeing me.

Gradually, as we waited, I took them all in. There was no one there that I knew, but somehow they all looked familiar. Or maybe I only thought they did, because when your eyes connected with someone's, they didn't quickly look away and they usually smiled. They were mostly women and children, and a few low-looking men. Some of them were white, which surprised me. I hadn't expected to see them in there.

Directly in front of the bench where we sat, a little girl with blond curls was trying to handle a bottle of Coke. Now and then, she'd manage to turn herself and the bottle around and watch me with big gray eyes that seemed to know quite well how badly I wanted a pop. I thought of asking Momma for fifteen cents so I could get one from the machine in the back, but I was afraid she'd still say no, so I just kept planning more and more convincing ways to ask. Besides, there was a water fountain near the door if I could make myself rise and walk to it.

We waited three hours. White ladies dressed like secretaries kept coming out to call numbers, and people on the benches would get up and follow down a hall. Then more people came in to replace them. I drank water from the fountain three times and was ready to put my feet up on the bench before us—the little girl with the Coke and her momma got called—by the time we heard Momma's number.

"You wait here," Momma said as I rose with her.

I sat down with a plop.

The lady with the number looked at me. Her face reminded me of the librarian's at Bunch school. Looked like she never cracked a smile. "Let her come," she said.

"She can wait here," Momma repeated weakly.

"It's OK. She can come in. Come on," the lady insisted at me.

I hesitated, knowing that Momma's face was telling me to sit.

"Come on," the woman said.

Momma said nothing.

I got up and followed them into the maze. We came to a small room where there was a desk and three chairs. The woman sat behind the desk, and we before it.

For a while, no one spoke. The woman studied a folder open before her, brows drawn together. On the wall behind her there was a calendar with one heavy black line drawn slantwise through each day of August, up to the twenty-first. That was today.

"Mrs. Blue, I have a notation here that Mr. Blue has not reported to the department on his efforts to obtain employment since the sixteenth of June. Before that, it was the tenth of April. You understand that department regulations require that he report monthly to this office, do you not?" Eyes brown as a wren's belly came up at Momma.

"Yes," Momma answered, sounding as small as I felt.

"Can you explain his failure to do so?"

Pause. "He's been looking. He says he's been looking."

"That may be. However, his failure to report those efforts here is my only concern."

Silence.

"We cannot continue with your case as it now stands if Mr. Blue refuses to comply with departmental regulations. He is still residing with the family, is he not?"

"Yes, he is. I've been reminding him to come in . . . he said he would."

"Well, he hasn't. Regulations are that any able-bodied man, head-of-household and receiving assistance, who neglects to report to this office any effort to obtain work for a period of sixty days or more is to be cut off for a minimum of three months, at which time he may reapply. As of this date, Mr. Blue is over sixty days delinquent, and officially, I am obliged to close the case and direct you to other sources of aid."

"What is that?"

"Aid to Dependent Children would be the only source available to you. Then, of course, you would not be eligible unless it was verified that Mr. Blue was no longer residing with the family."

Another silence. I stared into the gray steel front of the desk, everything stopped but my heart.

"Well, can you keep the case open until Monday? If he comes in by Monday?"

"According to my records, Mr. Blue failed to come in May, and such an agreement was made then. In all, we allowed him a period of seventy days. You must understand that what happens in such cases as this is not wholly my decision." She sighed and watched Momma with hopeless eyes, tapping the soft end of her pencil on the papers before her. "Mrs. Blue, I will speak to my superiors on your behalf. I can allow you until Monday next . . . that's the"—she swung around to the calendar—"twenty-sixth of August, to get him in here."

"Thank you. He'll be in," Momma breathed. "Will I be able to get the clothing order today?"

Hands and eyes searched in the folder for an answer before she cleared her throat and tilted her face at Momma. "We'll see what we can do," she said finally.

My back touched the chair. Without turning my head, I moved my eyes down to Momma's dusty feet and wondered if she could still feel them; my own were numb. I felt bodyless—there was only my face, which wouldn't disappear, and behind it, one word pinging against another in a buzz that made no sense. At home, we'd have the house cleaned by now, and I'd be waiting for the daily appearance of my best friend, Bernadine, so we could comb each other's hair or talk about stuck-up Evelyn and Brenda. Maybe Bernadine was already there, and Stella was teaching her to dance the bop.

Then I heard our names and ages—all eight of them—being called off like items in a grocery list.

"Clifford, Junior, age fourteen." She waited.

"Yes."

"Born? Give me the month and year."

"October 1946," Momma answered, and I could hear in her voice that she'd been through these questions before.

"Stella, age thirteen."

"Yes."

"Born?"

"November 1947."

"Minerva, age twelve." She looked at me. "This is Minerva?"

"Yes."

No. I thought, no, this is not Minerva. You can write it down if you want to, but Minerva is not here.

"Born?"

"December 1948."

The woman went on down the list, sounding more and more like Momma should be sorry or ashamed, and Momma's answers grew fainter and fainter. So this was welfare. I wondered how many times Momma had had to do this. Once before? Three times? Every time?

More questions. How many in school? Six. Who needs shoes? Everybody.

"Everybody needs shoes? The youngest two?"

"Well, they don't go to school . . . but they walk."

My head came up to look at Momma and the woman. The woman's mouth was left open. Momma didn't blink.

The brown eyes went down. "Our allowances are based on the median costs for moderately priced clothing at Sears, Roebuck." She figured on paper as she spoke. "That will mean thirty-four dollars for children over ten . . . thirty dollars for children under ten. It comes to one hundred ninety-eight dollars. I can allow eight dollars for two additional pairs of shoes."

"Thank you."

"You will present your clothing order to a salesperson at the store, who will be happy to assist you in your selections. Please be practical, as further clothing requests will not be considered for a period of six months. In cases of necessity, however, requests for winter outerwear will be considered beginning November first."

Momma said nothing.

The woman rose and left the room.

For the first time, I shifted in the chair. Momma was looking into the calendar as though she could see through the pages to November first. Everybody needed a coat.

I'm never coming here again, I thought. If I do, I'll stay out front. Not coming back in here. Ever again.

She came back and sat behind her desk. "Mrs. Blue, I must make it clear that, regardless of my feelings, I will be forced to close your case if your husband does not report to this office by Monday, the twenty-sixth. Do you understand?"

"Yes. Thank you. He'll come. I'll see to it."

"Very well." She held a paper out to Momma.

We stood. Momma reached over and took the slip of paper. I moved toward the door.

"Excuse me, Mrs. Blue, but are you pregnant?"

"What?"

"I asked if you were expecting another child."

"Oh. No, I'm not," Momma answered, biting down on her lips.

"Well, I'm sure you'll want to be careful about a thing like that in your present situation."

"Yes."

I looked quickly to Momma's loose white blouse. We'd never known when another baby was coming until it was almost there.

"I suppose that eight children are enough for anyone," the woman said, and for the first time her face broke into a smile.

Momma didn't answer that. Somehow, we left the room and found our way out onto the street. We stood for a moment, as though lost. My eyes followed Momma's up to where the sun was burning high. It was still there, blazing white against a cloudless blue. Slowly, Momma put the clothing order into her purse and snapped it shut. She looked around as if uncertain which way to go. I led the way to the corner. We turned. We walked the first five blocks.

I was thinking about how stupid I'd been a year ago, when Daddy lost his job. I'd been happy.

"You-all better be thinking about moving to Indianapolis," he announced one day after work, looking like he didn't think much of it himself. He was a welder with the railroad company. He'd worked there for eleven years. But now, "Company's moving to Indianapolis," he said. "Gonna be gone by November. If I want to keep my job, we've got to move with it."

We didn't. Nobody wanted to move to Indianapolis—not even Daddy. Here, we had uncles, aunts and cousins on both sides. Friends.

Everybody and everything we knew. Daddy could get another job. First came unemployment compensation. Then came welfare. Thank goodness for welfare, we said, while we waited and waited for the job that hadn't yet come.

The problem was that Daddy couldn't take it. If something got repossessed or somebody took sick or something was broken or another kid was coming, he'd carry on terribly until things got better—by which time things were always worse. He'd always been that way. So when the railroad left, he began to do everything wrong. Stayed out all hours. Drank and drank some more. When he was home, he was so grouchy we were afraid to squeak. Now when we saw him coming, we got lost. Even our friends ran for cover.

At the railroad tracks, we sped up. The tracks were as far across as a block was long. Silently, I counted the rails by the heat of the steel bars through my thin soles. On the other side, I felt something heavy rise up in my chest, and I knew that I wanted to cry. I wanted to cry or run or kiss the dusty ground. The little houses with their sun-scorched lawns and back-yard gardens were mansions in my eyes. "Ohh, Ma . . . look at those collards!"

"Umm-humm," she agreed, and I knew that she saw it too.

"Wonder how they grew so big?"

"Cow dung, probably. Big Poppa used to put cow dung out to fertilize the vegetable plots, and everything just grew like crazy. We used to get tomatoes this big"—she circled with her hands—"and don't talk about squash or melons."

"I bet y'all ate like rich people. Bet y'all had everything you could want."

"We sure did," she said. "We never wanted for anything when it came to food. And when the cash crops were sold, we could get whatever else that was needed. We never wanted for a thing."

"What about the time you and cousin Emma threw out the supper peas?"

"Oh! Did I tell you about that?" she asked. Then she told it all over again. I didn't listen. I watched her face and guarded her smile with a smile of my own.

We walked together, step for step. The sun was still burning, but we forgot to mind it. We talked about an Alabama girlhood in a time and place I'd never know. We talked about the wringer washer and how it could be fixed, because washing every day on a scrub board was something Alabama could keep. We talked about how to get Daddy to the Department of Social Services.

Then we talked about having babies. She began to tell me things I'd never known, and the idea of womanhood blossomed in my mind like some kind of suffocating rose.

"Momma," I said, "I don't think I can be a woman."

"You can," she laughed, "and if you live, you will be. You gotta be some kind of woman."

"But it's hard," I said. "Sometimes it must be hard."

"Umm-humm," she said, "sometimes it is hard."

When we got to the bad block, we crossed to Beaman's drugstore for two orange crushes. Then we walked right through the groups of men standing in the shadows of the poolroom and the Moonflower Hotel. Not one of them said a word to us. I supposed they could see in the way we walked that we weren't afraid. We'd been to the welfare office and back again. And the facts of life, fixed in our minds like the sun in the sky, were no burning mysteries. ◌

Nikki-Rosa

NIKKI GIOVANNI

childhood remembrances are always a drag
if you're Black
you always remember things like living in Woodlawn
with no inside toilet
and if you become famous or something
they never talk about how happy you were to have your mother
all to yourself and
how good the water felt when you got your bath from one of those
big tubs that folk in chicago barbecue in
and somehow when you talk about home
it never gets across how much you
understood their feelings
as the whole family attended meetings about Hollydale
and even though you remember
your biographers never understand
your father's pain as he sells his stock
and another dream goes
And though you're poor it isn't poverty that
concerns you

and though they fought a lot
it isn't your father's drinking that makes any difference
but only that everybody is together and you
and your sister have happy birthdays and very good christmasses
and I really hope no white person ever has cause to write about me
because they never understand Black love is Black wealth and they'll
probably talk about my hard childhood and never understand that
all the while I was quite happy

Phoenix Farm

JANE YOLEN

We moved into Grandma's farm right after our apartment house burned down along with most of the neighborhood. Even without the fire, it had not been a good California summer, dry as popcorn and twice as salty, what with all the sweat running down our faces.

I didn't mind so much—the fire, I mean. I had hated that apartment, with its pockmarked walls and the gang names scribbled on the stoop. Under my bedroom window someone had painted the words "Someday, sugar, you gonna find no one in this world gonna give you sweet." The grammar bothered me more than what it said.

Mama cried, though. About the photos, mostly. And about all her shoes having burned up. She has real tiny feet and her one vanity is shoes. She can buy the model stuff for really cheap. But it's not just the photos and the shoes. She cries about everything these days. It's been that way since Daddy died.

Ran off. That's what Nicky says. A week before the fire. *Couldn't take it. The recession and all. No job. No hope.*

Mama says it won't be forever, but I say he died. I can deal with it that way.

And besides, we don't want him back.

So we got ready to head for Grandma's farm up in the valley, with only the clothes we'd been wearing; our cat, Tambourine; and Mama's track medals, all fused together. She found them when the firefighters let us go back upstairs to sort through things. Nicky grabbed a souvenir, too. His old basketball. It was flat and blackened, like a pancake someone left on the stove too long.

I looked around and there was nothing I wanted to take. Nothing. All that I cared about had made it through the fire: Mama, Nicky, and Tam. It was as if we could start afresh and all the rest of it had been burned away. But as we were going down the stairs—the iron stairs, not the wooden ones inside, which were all gone—I saw the most surprising thing. On the thirteenth step up from the bottom, tucked against the riser, was a nest. It was unburnt, unmarked, the straw that held it the rubbed-off gold of a wheat field. A piece of red string ran through it, almost as if it had been woven on a loom. In the nest was a single egg.

It didn't look like any egg I'd ever seen before, not dull white or tan like the eggs from the store. Not even a light blue like the robin's egg I'd found the one summer we'd spent with Grandma at the farm. This was a shiny, shimmery gray-green egg with a red vein—the red thread—cutting it in half.

"Look!" I called out. But Mama and Nicky were already in the car, waiting. So without thinking it all the way through—like, what was I going to do with an egg, and what about the egg's mother, and what if it broke in the car or, worse, hatched—I picked it up and stuck it in the pocket of my jacket. Then, on second thought, I took off the jacket and made a kind of nest of it, and carefully carried the egg and my jacket down the rest of the stairs.

When I got into the car, it was the very first time I had ever ridden in the back all alone without complaining. And all the way to the farm, I kept the jacket-nest and its egg in my lap. All the way.

Grandma welcomed us, saying, "I'm not surprised. Didn't I tell you?" Meaning that Daddy wasn't with us. She and Mama didn't fight over it, which was a surprise on its own. Neighbors of Grandma's had collected clothes for us. It made us feel like refugees, which is an awkward feeling that makes you prickly and cranky most of the time. At least that's how I felt until I found a green sweater that exactly matches my eyes and Nicky found a Grateful Dead T-shirt. There were no shoes Mama's size. And no jobs nearby, either.

I stashed the egg in its jacket-nest on the dresser Mama and I shared. Nicky, being the only boy, got his own room. Mama never said a word about the egg. It was like she didn't even see it. I worried what she'd say if it began to smell.

But the days went by and the egg never did begin to stink. We got settled into our new school. I only thought about Daddy every *other* day.

And I found a best friend right away. Nicky had girls calling him after dinner for the first time. So we were OK.

Mama wasn't happy, though. She and Grandma didn't exactly quarrel, but they didn't exactly get along, either. Being thankful to someone doesn't make you like them. And since Mama couldn't find a job, they were together all day long.

Then one evening my new best friend, Ann Marie, was over. We were doing homework together up in my room. It was one of those coolish evenings and the windows were closed, but it was still pretty bright outside, considering.

Ann Marie suddenly said, "Look! Your egg is cracking open."

I looked up and she was right. We hadn't noticed anything before, because the crack had run along the red line. When I put my finger on the crack, it seemed to pulse.

"Feel that!" I said.

Ann Marie touched it, then jerked back as if she had been burned. "I'm going home now," she said.

"But, Ann Marie, aren't you the one who dragged me to see all those horror movies and—"

"Movies aren't real," she said. She grabbed up her books and ran from the room.

I didn't even say good-bye. The egg had all my attention, for the gray-green shell seemed to be taking little breaths, pulsing in and out, in and out, like a tiny brittle ocean. Then the crack widened, and as if there were a lamp inside, light poured out.

Nicky came in then, looking for some change on the dresser.

"Neat!" he said when he saw the light. "Do you know what kind of bird it's going to be? Did you look it up in Dad—" And then he stopped, because all of Daddy's books had been burned up. Besides, we didn't mention him anymore. And since we hadn't heard from him at all, it was like he really *was* dead.

"No," I said. "And I don't think it's any *ordinary* bird that you would find in an *ordinary* book."

"A lizard, you think?"

Never taking my eyes off the egg, I shook my head. How stupid could he be? With that light coming out? A dragon, maybe. Then the phone rang downstairs and he ran out of the room, expecting, I guess, that it would be Courtney or Brittany or another of his girlfriends named after spaniels. Talking to them was more important to him than my egg.

But I continued to watch. I was the only one watching when it hatched. How such a large bird got into such a small egg, I'll never know. But that's magic for you. It rose slowly out of the egg, pushing the top part of the shell with its golden head. Its beak was golden, too, and curved like one of those Arabian swords. Its eyes were hooded and dark, without a center. When it stared at me, I felt drawn in.

The bird gave a sudden kind of shudder and humped itself farther out of the egg, and its wings were blue and scarlet and gold, all shimmery, like some seashells when they're wet. It shook out its wings, and they were wide enough to touch from one side of the dresser to the other, the individual feathers throwing off sparkles of light.

Another shudder, and the bird stood free of the egg entirely, though a piece of shell still clung to the tip of one wing. I reached over and freed it, and it seared my fingers—the touch of the feather, not the shell. The bird's scarlet body and scaly golden feet pulsed with some kind of heat.

"What *are* you?" I whispered, then stuck my burnt fingers in my mouth to soothe them.

If the bird could answer me, it didn't; it just pumped its wings, which seemed to grow wider with each beat. The wind from them was a Santa Ana, hot and heavy and thick.

I ran to the window and flung it wide, holding the curtain aside.

The bird didn't seem to notice my effort, but still it flew unerringly outside. I saw it land once on a fencepost; a second time, on the roof of Grandma's barn. Then it headed straight toward the city, the setting sun making a fire in its feathers.

When I couldn't see it anymore, I turned around. The room smelled odd—like the ashes of a fire, but like something else, too. Cinnamon, maybe. Or cloves.

I heard the doorbell. It rang once, then a second time. Grandma and Mama were off visiting a neighbor. Nicky was still on the phone. I ran down the stairs and flung the door wide open.

Daddy was standing there, a new beard on his face and a great big Madame Alexander doll in his arms.

"I got a job, baby. In Phoenix. And a house rented. With a real backyard. I didn't know about the fire, I didn't know where you all had gone. My letters came back and the phone didn't connect and . . . ."

"Daddy!" I shouted, and he dropped the box to scoop me up against his chest. As I snuggled my face against his neck, I smelled that same smell: ashes and cinnamon, maybe cloves. Where my burnt fingers tangled in his hair they hurt horribly.

Grandma would be furious. Nicky and Mama might be, too. But I didn't care. There's dead. And there's not.

Sometimes it's better to rise up out of the ashes, singing. ∾

Responding to Cluster Three

How do families deal with problems?

Thinking Skill EVALUATING

1. In "The Charmer" from Cluster Two and "Somebody's Son" of this cluster, two troubled sons leave home. **Evaluate**, or judge, the actions of the main characters. Why do you think one returned home and one did not?

2. The hardships of divorce are shared in "After the Divorce" and "Gillian, Age Thirteen." Pick out at least one significant quotation from each selection and **evaluate** how you feel it is important to the topic of divorce.

3. **Evaluate** the attitudes that Minerva and Nikki have about poverty in "Getting the Facts of Life" and "Nikki-Rosa." Do you agree with these attitudes? Why or why not?

4. **Symbols** in literature are objects that represent an abstract idea. Look up the definition of the word phoenix. What do you think the phoenix symbolizes in "Phoenix Farm"?

5. Choose one person from this book that you would want as a brother or sister. Explain your choice.

Writing Activity: Evaluating Family Problems

Select three characters from this cluster and briefly describe the main problem faced by the family in the story. Then **evaluate** how the family deals with the problem. In your opinion, which family deals with their problem most successfully? Be prepared to explain your choice. You may want to use a chart such as the one below.

Selection	Main Problem	How Family Deals with Problem
Somebody's Son		
After the Divorce		
Gillian, Age Thirteen		
Getting the Facts of Life		
Nikki-Rosa		
Phoenix Farm		

A Strong Evaluation

- looks at both the details and the main ideas
- discovers and summarizes findings
- states an opinion or judgment based on the findings
- portrays a value judgment in the conclusion

CLUSTER FOUR

Thinking on Your Own

Thinking Skill SYNTHESIZING

Clear Glass Marbles

JANE MARTIN

*A young woman is standing next to an end table with a lamp on it,
holding a crystal bowl filled with ninety clear glass marbles.*

LAURIE

The day my mother found out she was dying she asked me to go out and buy her these clear glass marbles. Dad and I hadn't even known she was ill which was nothing new. Whenever you asked my mother if she was ill she would throw things at you, sesame buns, the editorial page, a handful of hair ribbons. "Do not," she would say, "suggest things to suggestible people." Anyway, I brought her the marbles and she counted ninety of them out and put them in this old cut-glass bowl which had been the sum total of great Aunt Helena's estate.[1] Apparently, the doctor had given her three months and she set great store by doctors. She said she always believed them because they were the nearest thing to the Old Testament we had. "I wouldn't give you two bits for these young smiley guys," she'd say, "I go for a good, stern-furrowed physican." She wouldn't even have her teeth cleaned by a dentist under fifty. So she counted out ninety clear glass marbles and set them in the bowl on her bedside table. Then she went out and spent twelve hundred dollars on nightgowns. She said, "In my family you are only dying when you take to your bed, and that, my darlings, is where I am going." And she did.

1 **estate:** property left by a person at death

Oh we hashed it around. Dad said she couldn't possibly be dying but the doctors convinced him. I told her it seemed a little medieval[2] to lie in state[3] up there but she said she didn't want to be distracted from what she loved, us, and what she wanted to mull . . . And she said there was nothing outside except drugstores and supermarkets and drycleaners and that given her situation they were beneath her dignity. I asked her what she intended to do up there and she said study French, visit with us, generally mull and maybe call a few pals. Study French. She said she had made a pledge to herself years ago that she would die bilingual. Dad and I cried a lot, but she didn't. He was fun to cry with. From then on the doctors had to come see *her* because, as she put it, she *came in* with a house call and she was *going out* with a house call. And all day, every day, she would hold one of these marbles in her hand. Why? She said it made the day longer. Mother had her own bedroom. That was the way it always was, for as long as I can remember. She called my father "The Thrasher." Dad could really get into a nightmare. Apparently early on in the marriage he had flipped over and broken her nose and that was it. Separate beds. Her room was very spare really. Wooden floors, an old steel-and-brass bed, oak dresser, bedside table, and don't ask me why, a hat rack. No pictures on the walls. She never understood how people could look at the same darn thing day after day. She said it was bound to "deflate the imagination." We'd sit with her after dinner and talk about "issues." She told us she was too far gone for gossip or what we ate for lunch. Then we'd all turn in and in a little while, just before I'd drift off I'd hear this . . .* *(She rolls one of the marbles across the stage floor.)* Happened every night. After the third or fourth day I saw one on the floor and started to pick it up but she said "leave it." She said it very sharply. I asked, "How come?" She said she was "learning to let go of them." *(From now on the actress frequently rolls marbles across the stage, indicated hereafter by an asterisk, ending up at last with only one.)* Oh, she passed the time. There were things she wanted. She made out a list of children's books from her own childhood and we got as many of them as we could find from the library. She said they were still the only good books she'd ever read.*

She wrote notes to, I don't know, maybe sixty or seventy people, and they told us later on that they were sort of little formal goodbyes, each of

2 **medieval:** extremely outdated
3 **lie in state:** honor given to body before burial

them recalling some incident or shared something, not very significant, but the odd thing was that in each one she included a recipe. A recipe in every one of them.

We got out the big cookie tin full of snapshots that somehow never became a scrapbook. She liked that. She showed my father how to do the medical insurance and how she handled the accounts. We went through her jewelry.* She wrote down the names of the roofers and plumbers and air-conditioning people. She called it "wrapping it up." "Well, this is good," she'd say, "I'm wrapping it up."*

She had the television moved up in her room and she called me aside to say that it was entirely possible that she might reach a stage where she really wouldn't know what she was watching but that I must promise her that I'd keep it on P.B.S.[4]

Later on, when it started getting hard,* she told Dad and me that she would like to spend more time alone. "I'm afraid," she said, "that I'm going to have to do this more or less by myself." She said that she was glad, and she hoped we would be, that this was arranged so that you got less attached to the people you loved at the end. The next period isn't worth going into, it was just . . . hard. *(She picks up the bowl of marbles.)* Do you know that from the very beginning down to the very last she never admitted to any pain. Never. She called it "the chills." The last thing she asked for was a picture we had in the front entrance hall of a labrador retriever she and Dad had owned when they were first married. He was, she said, a perfectly dreadful dog. "When you are young," she said, "you believe in the perfectibility of dogs."

I was in bed two weeks ago Wednesday toward dawn, then this . . . *(She pours the rest of the marbles on the floor. When they have stopped rolling, she speaks.)* Dad and I ran in there. The bedside table was turned over and she was gone. Dead. When the emergency medical people got there they found this . . . *(She opens her hand to disclose one more marble.)* The rest spilled when the table fell, but this one was still in her hand.

I keep it.

I keep it in my hand all day.

It makes the day longer.

BLACKOUT ∾

4 **P.B.S.:** Public Broadcasting System

Trust Me

FREDERICK WATERMAN

The sense of betrayal was the hardest part," I said.

"Understandably so," replied Jean-Louis Bertrand, my late father's lawyer. "And that was the hardest thing for him, too. We talked about it for many, many hours."

I was sitting next to Bertrand on the late-afternoon flight from Paris to Zürich.

"You talked more with my father than I ever did."

"That is probably true."

"And shared more secrets."

"That is certainly true."

"Secrets that I'm never going to learn about."

"That was your father's request."

I glanced at the man in seat B. He was in his early 60s, wore wire-rim glasses, and had on a dark-blue suit, white shirt, and perfectly knotted tie. M. Bertrand sat with his hands clasped before him, fingers interlocked. His appearance was as precise as his words.

"You knew everything that was going to happen, didn't you, Monsieur Bertrand?"

"Yes, I did."

"Was it your idea?"

"No. When your father called me about this, he didn't ask for my opinion; he simply gave me instructions."

"And it all happened as he expected?"

"Yes. You were the only uncertainty—at least that's what I thought. But your father told me, in fact, that you were the one certainty. He was absolutely sure of you."

The words pleased me, for I am, like all other sons, attuned to any compliment from my father.

Bertrand continued, "Because of a letter, he said that he had no doubt about you. I believe he wrote it when you were quite young."

"I was 15," I answered. "We weren't on speaking terms then—I don't remember why."

But I did remember the letter, left on my pillow one night. I remember because it was the foundation for our future relationship. It was the reaching out of a wise father to a difficult son. Over the years, I've read those five sentences so many times that I've memorized them.

"Henri—I don't know which it is, that we are too different or we are too similar, but I fear that we will fail as father and son. We have fought and argued for too long, and so I suggest a truce. What I offer are two things: a promise that I will never lie to you, and a promise that I will never be unfair to you. In return, I only ask one thing—that you trust me. I won't ask for your love, and I won't even ask that you like me, but in those days or years that you hate me, if you trust me, we will never lose each other."

And my father's instinct proved correct. Holding on to those words, we reached a middle ground that was tentatively approached then firmly claimed. I believe that he never lied to me, and, until he died, I never had reason to think he had been unfair. So I trusted him, and it was out of that trust that I came to love him.

I remember my father's long, laughing conversations with my mother and Bertrand, his two closest friends. He and I could never talk that way; our words and thoughts never seemed to blend, but, because of his letter, we became the closest of strangers.

But the three months since his death had thrown me back into an almost adolescent roller-coaster of emotions. I was disappointed and hurt, angry at him and angry at myself. I felt betrayed and foolish for having trusted him so much.

"Your response was crucial," continued Bertrand. "I was struck by how much faith your father put in you. He said that the two of you had an agreement, and that despite every appearance, every circumstance, you'd keep your word."

Blind faith, I thought. Everyone needs to believe in something, and the first thing that children believe in is their parents. We don't want them to be fallible, but finally we yield and let them be human.

I never knew all the corners of my father's life. I did know that he was born in Switzerland, moved to France in his early 20s, and quickly made a fortune leasing and subleasing commercial properties. His business interests branched out and eventually reached around the world, from Singapore to Miami and Oslo to Johannesburg, where he met the young woman who became my mother.

Much of my father's success was due to an odd quirk of visual imagination, for he could correctly predict the direction and timing of a young city's growth. He could see where and when, pressured by population and industry, a city would break through its boundaries. My father would rent a small plane and fly over a city for hours, first recognizing why the earliest settlement had been placed there, and then in ever-widening circles he would gradually work his way out, studying the roads, the rivers, and the contours of the land until he could picture the next inevitable surge of expansion.

He would buy several large properties, usually farms that could be rented back to the farmers for a few years, until the businessmen without foresight arrived, ready to pay 50- or 100-fold for their sudden need to build roads, homes, and stores. My father would sell and move on.

And there were other businesses, highly profitable ones, that my father would not talk about, though I knew they involved oddly circuitous[1] routes for imports and exports. These profits were quickly converted into invisible investments, specifically diamonds, rare stamps, and coins that would appear in no bank account, stock portfolio, or corporate record. And this portion of my father's wealth grew without a taxable trace. Because of his visual imagination, it was perhaps inevitable that he would develop an interest in art. Over the next 20 years, the diamonds, stamps, and coins were converted into nearly 100 extraordinary paintings.

Other works—sketches, drawings, and sculptures—were on display throughout the house, but the paintings were all held in one wing, carefully framed and hung in two large rooms where my father could often be found, sitting in front of any one painting for an hour or more. I once asked him why, and he explained, "With a bad artist, in five minutes you'll see everything that he put into the painting. With a genius, the longer you look, the more you see."

I did not have my father's eye for art, but there was one picture I grew to love. It was by Canfield, a little-known English painter of the 1800s, and showed two burly workmen sitting atop a partially built stone wall, rocks

---

1 **circuitous:** circular or winding

strewn about their feet. Their hats pushed back on their heads, they were eating a simple meal of bread and cheese and talking to each other. Both men, eyes twinkling, were on the verge of laughter. I understood myself well enough to know why I liked Canfield's painting so much.

My father's judgment on all things business was perfect. The only major mistake that he made in his life was understandable, for it has been made by thousands of other widowers. The young woman looked just like my mother had at the age of 30. Blonde, slender, and with soft blue eyes, she even spoke with the same gentle South African accent.

Sylvia was indeed beautiful, and her charm pulled my father ever deeper in love. Their courtship was quick and the marriage inevitable. I was my father's best man, and I was glad for him, for I, too, had been fooled. It was more than a year before his first doubt formed; then he became more alert to her words and actions and realized that she was not in love with him and never had been. My father had been convenient, as rich men often are. And he knew that every morning he was waking up next to a woman who didn't love him. Sylvia, sensing his awareness, stopped putting up any pretense.

She did not cheat on him—under French law, that would have jeopardized the marriage. As M. Bertrand explained to my father, as long as Sylvia committed no overt acts and remained "an innocent party," she could delay a divorce for six years and thus remain the cosseted[2] wife of a multimillionaire. Whichever path my father chose would be an expensive one. Before he could make his choice, the fates intervened.

Cancer of the pancreas is brutally swift. The first diagnosis gave him three months; the second opinion was for two. And, as he wasted away, I never saw a moment's grief in Sylvia's eyes. Her timing had been impeccable.[3] Marry a rich man; then watch him die—it was the dream of every black widow.[4]

I never asked my father why he hadn't required a prenuptial agreement[5] from Sylvia, but he offered an answer anyway. "I thought I'd found your mother again—and I couldn't imagine her being dishonest."

During my father's last months, I visited as often as my schedule, that of a university assistant professor, would allow. And I saw how much time Sylvia spent in the paintings wing. She had no love for the art, only

---

2 **cosseted:** pampered

3 **impeccable:** fautless; blameless

4 **black widow:** greedy woman seemingly unmoved by husband's death

5 **prenuptial agreement:** contract between partners made before marriage

for its value, and she knew how much my father had paid for each work. She figured, rightly, that their sum value would be between 240 and 330 million francs,[6] depending upon how much excitement was generated by their auction.

In the art world, there are always doubts and suspicions because fakes have tricked even the best art experts, but microscopes do not lie. It was Bertrand who suggested a scientific testing of the collection to confirm the age of each work, and Sylvia immediately championed this idea. Microscopic specks of paint, taken from beneath the pictures' frames, were sent to a laboratory in London that specialized in spectroscopic analysis.

One week later, the test results were returned. My father's eye for genius had been validated. Every picture was genuine.

During my father's illness, I often sat with him, and each day—no matter how weak he felt—he would ask to go to the paintings wing. There was nothing to him by then, so we did not bother with wheelchairs and elevators. I would pick him up and carry him downstairs, where he would name a picture—occasionally the Canfield—and I would place him in a chair before it. He would sit there, studying his familiar friend until he drifted off, then I'd return him to his bed.

I could not be at my father's side every day, nor could Bertrand, but Sylvia was always there. For two months, she drilled into my father that he owed her complete security for the rest of her life, that it was his duty to take care of her, and how she'd given up her career for him. When I arrived at the house, it was often to the sound of her raised voice, telling my father what she "deserved."

During his last two days, sedated by painkillers, my father drifted in and out of consciousness as I sat next to his bed, holding his hand. One afternoon, when I thought he was asleep, he gripped my hand with sudden strength, and his eyes opened with absolute clarity.

"Do you still trust me?" His voice was an intense whisper.

"I always have."

"Don't ever stop."

I hid my confusion and gave him my word. After a long moment, my father's hand lost its strength again and his eyes faded back into bleary confusion. Four hours later, I took my hand from his, for he was no longer there.

---

6 **francs:** units of money in France

It was five days later that Sylvia, her lawyer, and I sat in M. Bertrand's office for the reading of the will.

What I remember most from that morning was Sylvia's joy. M. Bertrand, in his clear, clipped way, read aloud my father's words, which bequeathed to Sylvia the whole art collection—including Canfield's workmen. She had worn my father down and won. M. Bertrand continued, saying that 180,000 francs had been set aside for Sylvia's immediate use and that death duties would be paid by the sale of my father's house and land. The remainder of his estate, consolidated into one account at the Banque Nationale de Paris, would be mine. The math was simple—depending upon what the paintings brought at auction, Sylvia's share would be six to eight times what I received.

The final clause provided a three-month window for challenges by Sylvia or me. The paintings would be placed in a bank vault, and there would be no distributions until we both signed an irrevocable[7] agreement accepting our shares.

Sylvia conferred in a whisper with her lawyer, then announced, "We can take care of this right now. I have no disagreement with the will. I think it's very fair." She turned to me. "Are you going to contest your father's wishes?"

I was still too stunned to answer. "I'll reserve my right," was all I managed to say.

"This is what he wanted!" Sylvia replied, instantly adopting the righteous tone of the loyal widow.

"I'll reserve my right," I repeated.

She whispered again with her lawyer, who kept glancing at me and shaking his head. I guessed she was asking whether I could be forced to sign before the three months elapsed.

Bertrand, who had been named executor, said he would prepare an acceptance agreement that would be ready at our mutual convenience. Sylvia, without another word, stood up, directed a look of sneering disdain at me, and departed with her lawyer.

I looked at Bertrand. "This isn't what I expected."

"I know," he nodded.

"I'm willing to fight her."

"Your father hoped to spare you that battle."

"So he gave her everything she wanted!" I thought of Canfield's

7 **irrevocable:** not possible to take back

workmen and already missed them. I'd never asked, and my father had never promised, but I'd always hoped that I, too, would grow old looking at them.

"It doesn't seem fair," said Bertrand, "and it probably isn't. But your father understood that Sylvia is an accomplished and convincing liar. On the stand, she would cry and sob and play to perfection the role of the grieving widow, while subtly casting you as the greedy, grasping son. Remember, her pretense of love was so convincing that your father married her."

I looked at my copy of the will and saw that it was dated six weeks ago. "Do you believe that my father was of sound mind when he wrote this?"

"Honestly, I do," replied Bertrand. "I was present when he signed it. His mind and judgment were perfect. That's what I would have to testify to."

I left M. Bertrand's office and walked down rue de Galimon, then turned north on boulevard St-Michel, passed over the l'Ile de la Cité, and spent the rest of the day walking, thinking, and struggling to fit my father's final act to the truce we'd both lived by.

The extra money wasn't important; I would be rich enough. It was the betrayal of trust that took so long to accept. I needed the full three months to make peace with my father's decision.

An appointment was made with Bertrand, and, when I arrived, Sylvia's lawyer was already reviewing the agreement. When he finished, he looked at Sylvia and handed her a pen. She signed her name in the two required places. When I added my signatures, Sylvia officially became one of the wealthiest women in France.

Bertrand explained that it would take a few days to re-register the paintings in Sylvia's name. Then she could remove them from the bank vault and decide whether she wished to sell or keep them.

"Oh, of course I'm going to keep them." Her tone was mocking. "I love good art."

Bertrand did not react. He turned to me. "The account at BNP may be transferred at your convenience. Where do you wish the money to be sent?" I handed him a sheet of paper with wiring instructions. "Then I believe that we are finished," Bertrand concluded.

"It's been a pleasure," Sylvia said, and she marched out in triumph, her lawyer in her wake.

I remained seated in Bertrand's office. "I still don't believe it," I said finally.

"Don't dwell on it," he replied. "Your father believed this was for the best." Then he firmly turned the conversation in another direction. "Have you decided where you will scatter your father's ashes?"

"Yes. Outside Zurich, on the same mountain where he and I took my mother's ashes."

"When will you go?"

"Tomorrow or the next day." A trip, a change of some kind, would be good.

"If I might ask," said Bertrand, "I'd like to be there, too. It would mean a great deal to me. Could you wait 10 days?"

I didn't want to, but I would not refuse my father's friend.

"Thank you," he said. "And will you stay in Paris until then?"

I replied that I probably would.

It was three days later that *Le Monde* reported the first letter—sent to a family in Salzburg. The next day came reports of a dozen more letters, received in Bruges, Weisbaden, Marseilles, and Amsterdam. The following day, two dozen letters were delivered in the States. Every letter was addressed to a family and began with the same sentences: "During World War II, your family owned a beautiful painting that was stolen by the Third Reich. Your painting is now in the possession of a woman in Paris . . . ."

None of the nearly 100 letters was signed, but every letter was correct: All the pictures had been stolen, and Sylvia was the registered owner of every one of them. For the next week, the police and the press came to me and asked what I knew about my father's collection. I told them the truth, and they recognized my innocence; the problem, they decided, was not mine. Sylvia responded with defiant claims that every painting was legally hers. By the end of the 10 days, more than four dozen lawsuits had been lodged against her, including one that sought return of the Canfield. Later I would ask M. Bertrand to inquire whether the picture might be for sale.

I looked out the airplane's window at the majestic range of Switzerland's Jura Mountains. In a bag tucked beneath the seat was a heavy square box. Tomorrow, perhaps at dawn, M. Bertrand and I would travel south of Zürich, to the top of the Uetliberg,[8] and, when the morning breeze picked up, I would put my father's ashes into the air.

---

8 **Uetliberg:** mountain overlooking Zürich, Switzerland

"There is one last thing," said M. Bertrand, reaching into his jacket pocket. "This is for you."

I opened the flap of the white envelope, preparing myself for the familiar handwriting. I opened the folded page.

"Henri—Because this is in your hand, everything must have gone right, and I apologize for what I've put you through. You know about the paintings now, and I am embarrassed for having held them so long, knowing they were not mine. In my defense, I can only say that I made a deal with myself: I could buy and keep those wonderful works only if, at my death, they were returned to their rightful owners. When Sylvia showed who she really was, I was forced to add another step to their return. Bertrand did not like my new plan. He was worried for you, but I told him not to be, for the only things that I'm sure of in this world are that my son knows I will never lie to him and that I will never be unfair to him. And I know that he'll always trust me. I love you, Your Father." ❧

Father and Son

WILLIAM STAFFORD

No sound—a spell—on, on out
where the wind went, our kite sent back
its thrill along the string that
sagged but sang and said, "I'm here!
I'm here!"—till broke somewhere,
gone years ago, but sailed forever clear
of earth. I hold—whatever tugs
the other end—I hold that string.

Dancer

VICKIE SEARS

Tell you just how it was with her. Took her to a dance not long after she come to live with us. Smartest thing I ever done. Seems like some old Eaglespirit woman saw her living down here and came back just to be with Clarissa.

Five years old she was when she come to us. Some foster kids come with lots of stuff, but she came with everything she had in a paper bag. Some dresses that was too short. A pair of pants barely holding a crotch. A pile of ratty underwear and one new nightgown. Mine was her third foster home in as many months. The agency folks said she was *so-cio-path-ic*,[1] I don't know nothing from that. She just seemed like she was all full up with anger and scaredness like lots of the kids who come to me. Only she was a real loner. Not trusting nobody. But she ran just like any other kid, was quiet when needed. Smiled at all the right times. If you could get her to smile, that is. Didn't talk much, though.

Had these ferocious dreams, too. Real screamer dreams they were. Shake the soul right out of you. She'd be screaming and crying with her little body wriggling on the bed, her hair all matted up on her woody-colored face. One time I got her to tell me what she was seeing, and she told me how she was being chased by a man with a long knife what he was going to kill her with and nobody could hear her calling out for help. She didn't talk too much about them, but they was all bad like that one. Seemed the most fierce dreams I ever remember anybody ever having

---

1 *sociopathic*: antisocial

outside of a vision seek.[2] They said her tribe was Assiniboin,[3] but they weren't for certain. What was for sure was that she was a fine dark-eyed girl just meant for someone to scoop up for loving.

Took her to her first dance in September, like I said, not long after she came. It wasn't like I thought it would be a good thing to do. It was just that we was all going. Me, my own kids, some nieces and nephews and the other children who was living with us. The powwow was just part of what we done all the time. Every month. More often in the summer. But this was the regular first Friday night of the school year. We'd all gather up and go to the school. I was thinking on leaving her home with a sitter cause she'd tried to kill one of the cats a couple of days before. We'd had us a big talk and she was grounded, but, well, it seemed like she ought to be with us.

Harold, that's my oldest boy, he and the other kids was mad with her, but he decided to show her around anyhow. At the school he went through the gym telling people, "This here's my sister, Clarissa." Wasn't no fuss or anything. She was just another one of the kids. When they was done meeting folks, he put her on one of the bleachers near the drum and went to join the men. He was in that place where his voice cracks but was real proud to be drumming. Held his hand up to his ear even, some of the time. Anyhow, Clarissa was sitting there, not all that interested in the dance or drum, when Molly Graybull come out in her button dress. Her arms was all stretched out, and she was slipping around, preening on them spindles of legs that get skinnier with every year. She was well into her seventies, and I might as well admit, Molly had won herself a fair share of dance contests. So it wasn't no surprise how a little girl could get so fixated on Molly. Clarissa watched her move around-around-around. Then all the rest of the dancers after Molly. She sure took in a good eyeful. Fancy dance. Owl dance. Circle dance. Even a hoop dancer was visiting that night. Everything weaving all slow, then fast. Around-around until that child couldn't see nothing else. Seemed like she was struck silent in the night, too. Never had no dreams at all. Well, not the hollering kind anyways.

Next day she was more quiet than usual only I could see she was looking at her picture book and tapping the old one-two, one-two. Tapping her

---

2 **vision seek:** Native American rite in which a person seeks self-knowledge through several days of prayer and fasting

3 **Assiniboin:** nomadic Native American tribe found mostly in North Dakota, Montana, southern Manitoba and Saskatchewan

toes on the rug with the inside of her head going around and around. As quiet as she could be, she was.

A few days went on before she asks me, "When's there gonna be another dance?"

I tell her in three weeks. She just smiles and goes on outside, waiting on the older kids to come home from school.

The very next day she asks if she can listen to some singing. I give her the tape recorder and some of Joe Washington from up to the Lummi reservation and the Kicking Woman Singers.[4] Clarissa, she takes them tapes and runs out back behind the chicken shed, staying out all afternoon. I wasn't worried none, though, cause I could hear the music the whole time. Matter of fact, it like to make me sick of them same songs come the end of three weeks. But that kid, she didn't get into no kind of mischief. Almost abnormal how good she was. Worried me some to see her so caught up but it seemed good too. The angry part of her slowed down so's she wasn't hitting the animals or chopping on herself with sticks like she was doing when she first come. She wasn't laughing much either, but she started playing with the other kids when they come home. Seemed like everybody was working hard to be better with each other.

Come March, Clarissa asks, "Can I dance?"

For sure, the best time for teaching is when a kid wants to listen, so we stood side to side with me doing some steps. She followed along fine. I put on a tape and started moving faster, and Clarissa just kept up all natural. I could tell she'd been practicing lots. She was doing real good.

Comes the next powwow, which was outside on the track field, I braided Clarissa's hair. Did her up with some ermine[5] and bead ties, then give her a purse to carry. It was all beaded with a rose and leaves. Used to be my aunt's. She held it right next to her side with her chin real high. She joined in a Circle dance. I could see she was watching her feet a little and looking how others do their steps, but mostly she was doing wonderful. When Molly Graybull showed up beside her, Clarissa took a seat and stared. She didn't dance again that night, but I could see there was dreaming coming into her eyes. I saw that fire that said to practice. And she did. I heard her every day in her room. Finally bought her her very own tape recorder so's the rest of us could listen to music too.

---

4 **Kicking Woman Singers:** Native American pow-pow musicians

5 **ermine:** weasel coat

Some months passed on. All the kids was getting bigger. Clarissa, she went into the first grade. Harold went off to community college up in Seattle, and that left me with Ronnie being the oldest at home. Clarissa was keeping herself busy all the time going over to Molly Graybull's. She was coming home with Spider Woman stories and trickster tales. One night she speaks up at supper and says, right clear and loud, "I'm an Assiniboin." Clear as it can be, she says it again. Don't nobody have to say nothing to something that proud said.

Next day I started working on a wing dress for Clarissa. She was going to be needing one for sure real soon.

Comes the first school year powwow and everyone was putting on their best. I called for Clarissa to come to my room. I told her, "I think it's time you have something special for yourself." Then I held up the green satin and saw her eyes full up with glitter. She didn't say nothing. Only kisses me and runs off to her room.

Just as we're all getting out of the car, Clarissa whispered to me, "I'm gonna dance with Molly Graybull." I put my hand on her shoulder to say, "You just listen to your spirit. That's where your music is."

We all danced an Owl dance, a Friendship dance, and a couple of Circle dances. Things was feeling real warm and good, and then it was time for the women's traditional. Clarissa joined the circle. She opened her arms to something nobody but her seemed to hear. That's when I saw that old Eagle woman come down and slide right inside of Clarissa, scooping up that child. There Clarissa was, full up with music. All full with that old, old spirit, letting herself dance through Clarissa's feet. Then Molly Graybull come dancing alongside Clarissa, and they was both the same age. ౧

As It Is with Strangers

SUSAN BETH PFEFFER

It wasn't until right before I went to bed on Thursday that Mom bothered to tell me the son she'd given up for adoption twenty years earlier was coming over for supper the next day.

"What son?" I asked.

"I'm sure I've told you about him," Mom said. "You must have forgotten."

I figured I probably had. I'm always forgetting little things like my homework assignments and being elected President of the United States. Having an older brother must have just slipped my mind. "How'd you two find each other?" I asked. Presumably Mom had never told me that.

"I registered with an agency," she said. "Put my name and address in a book, so if he ever wanted to find me, he could. I guess he did. Don't be late for supper tomorrow."

"I won't be," I promised. This was one reunion I had no intention of missing.

School the next day really dragged on. School never goes fast on Fridays, but when your mind is on some newly acquired half brother, it's real hard to care about Julius Caesar.[1] I didn't tell anybody, though. It seemed to me it was Mom's story, not mine, and besides, my friends all think she's crazy anyway. Probably from things I've said over the years.

---

1 **Julius Caesar:** famous Roman emperor

I went straight home from school, and was surprised, first to find the place spotless, and then to see Mom in the kitchen cooking away.

"I took a sick day," she informed me. "So I could prepare better."

"Everything looks great," I told her. It was true. I hadn't seen the place look so good since Great-Aunt Trudy came with the goat, but that's another story. "You look very pretty too."

"I got my nails done," Mom said, showing them off for me. They were coral colored. "And my hair."

I nodded. Mom had taught me that nothing was unbearable if your hair looked nice.

"Is that what you're planning to wear tonight?" she asked.

"I thought I'd shower and change into my dress," I said. I own a grand total of one dress, but this seemed to be the right kind of occasion for it.

Mom gave me a smile like I'd just been canonized.[2] "Thank you," she said. "Tonight's kind of important for me."

I nodded. I wasn't sure just what to say anymore. Mom and I have been alone for eight years, and you'd figure by now I'd know how to handle her under any circumstances, but this one had me stumped. "What's for supper?" I finally asked.

"Southern fried chicken," Mom said. "At first I thought I'd make a roast, but then what if he doesn't like his meat rare? And turkey seemed too Thanksgivingish, if you know what I mean. Everybody likes fried chicken. And I made mashed potatoes and biscuits and a spinach salad."

"Spinach salad?" I asked. I could picture Mom pouring the spinach out of a can and dousing it with Wishbone.

"From scratch," Mom informed me. "Everything's from scratch. And I baked an apple pie too. The ice cream is store bought, but I got one of those expensive brands. What do you think?"

I thought that there obviously was something to that Prodigal Son story, since Mom never made anything more elaborate for me than scrambled eggs. "It smells great," I said. It did, too, the way you picture a house in a commercial smelling, all homey and warm. "I'm sure everything will go fine."

"I want it to," Mom said, as though I'd suggested that maybe she didn't.

There were a few things I knew I'd better clear up before Big Brother showed up. "What's his name?" I asked, for starters.

2 **canonized:** declared to be a saint

"Jack," Mom said. "That's not what I would have named him. I would have named him Ronald."

"You would have?" I asked. I personally am named Tiffany, and Ronald would not have been my first guess.

"That was my boyfriend's name," Mom said. "Ronny."

"Your boyfriend," I said. "You mean his father?"

Mom nodded. "You think of them as boyfriends, not fathers, when you're sixteen," she said.

Well that answered question number two. It had seemed unlikely to me that my father was responsible, but who knew? I wasn't there. Maybe he and Mom had decided they wanted a girl, and chucked out any boys that came along first.

Speaking of which. "There aren't any other brothers I've forgotten about?" I asked. "Is this going to be the first of many such dinners?"

"Jack's the only one," Mom replied. "I wanted to keep him, but Ronny wasn't about to get married, and Dad said if I gave him up for adoption then I could still go to college. I did the right thing, for him and for me. And I would have gone to college if I hadn't met your father. I don't know. Maybe because I gave up the baby, I was too eager to get married. I never really thought about it."

"Did Dad know?" I asked.

"I told him," Mom said. "He said it didn't matter to him. And it didn't. Whatever else was wrong in our marriage, he never threw the baby in my face."

I found myself picturing a baby being thrown in Mom's face, and decided I should take my shower fast. So I sniffed the kitchen appreciatively and scurried out. In the shower I tried to imagine what this Jack would look like, but he kept resembling Dad's high-school graduation picture, which made no sense biologically at all. So I stopped imagining.

When I went to my bedroom to change, though, I was really shocked. Mom had extended her cleaning ways to include my room. All my carefully laid out messes were gone. It would probably take me months to reassemble things. I considered screaming at Mom about the sanctity³ of one's bedroom, but I decided against it. Mom obviously wanted this guy to think she and I were the perfect American family, and if that meant even my room had to be clean, then nothing was going to stop her. I could live with it, at least for the evening.

Mom and I set the table three times before the doorbell finally rang. When it did, neither one of us knew who should answer it, but Mom finally opened the door. "Hello," this guy said. "I'm Jack."

"I'm Linda," Mom replied. "Come on in. It's nice to . . . well, it's good seeing you."

"Good to see you too," Jack said. He didn't look anything like my father.

"This is Tiffany," Mom said. "She, uh . . ."

"Her daughter," I said. "Your sister." I mean, those words were going to be used at some point during the evening. We might as well get them out of the way fast. Then when we got around to the big tricky words like *mother* and *son*, at least some groundwork would have been laid.

"It's nice to meet you," Jack said, and he gave me his hand to shake, so I shook it. They say you can tell a lot about a man from his handshake,

---

3 **sanctity:** sacredness; security

but not when he's your long-lost brother. "I hope my coming like this isn't any kind of a brother. I mean bother."

"Not at all," Mom said. "I'm going to check on dinner. Tiffany, why don't you show Jack the living room? I'll join you in a moment."

"This is the living room," I said, which was pretty easy to show Jack, since we were already standing in it. "Want to sit down?"

"Yeah, sure," Jack said. "Have you lived here long?"

"Since the divorce," I said. "Eight years ago."

"That long," Jack said. "Where's your father?"

"He lives in Oak Ridge," I said. "That's a couple of hundred miles from here. I see him sometimes."

"Is he . . ." Jack began. "I mean, I don't suppose you'd know . . ."

"Is he your father too?" I said. "No. I kind of asked. Your father's name is Ronny. My father's name is Mike. I don't know much else about your father except he didn't want to marry Mom. They were both teenagers, I guess. Do you want to meet him too?"

"Sometime," Jack said. "Not tonight."

I could sure understand that one. "I've always wanted to have a big brother," I told him. "I always had crushes on my friends' big brothers. Did you want that—to have a kid sister, I mean?"

"I have one," Jack said. "No, I guess now I have two. I have a sister back home. Her name is Leigh Ann. She's adopted too. She's Korean."

"Oh," I said. "That's nice. I guess there isn't much of a family resemblance, then."

"Not much," Jack said, but he smiled. "She's twelve. How old are you?"

"Fifteen," I said. "Do you go to college?"

Jack nodded. "I'm a sophomore at Bucknell," he said. "Do you think you'll go to college?"

"I'd like to," I said. "I don't know if we'll have the money, though."

"It's rough," Jack said. "College costs a lot these days. My father's always griping about it. He owns a car dealership. New and used. I work there summers. My mom's a housewife."

I wanted to tell him how hard Mom had worked on supper, how messy the apartment usually was, how I never wore a dress, and Mom's nails were always a deep sinful scarlet. I wanted to tell him that maybe someday I'd be jealous that he'd been given away to a family that could afford to send him to college, but that it was too soon for me to feel much of anything about him. There was a lot I wanted to say, but I didn't say any of it.

"What's she like?" Jack asked me, and he gestured toward the kitchen, as though I might not otherwise know who he was talking about.

"Mom?" I said. "She's terrible. She drinks and she gambles and she beats me black and blue if I even think something wrong."

Jack looked horrified. I realized he had definitely not inherited Mom's sense of humor.

"I'm only kidding," I said. "I haven't even been spanked since I was five. She's fine. She's a good mother. It must have really hurt her to give you away like that."

"Have you known long?" Jack asked. "About me?"

"Not until recently," I said. It didn't seem right to tell him I'd learned less than twenty-four hours before. "I guess Mom was waiting until I was old enough to understand."

"I always knew I was adopted," Jack said. "And for years I've wanted to meet my biological parents. To see what they looked like. I love Mom and Dad, you understand. But I felt this need."

"I can imagine," I said, and I could too. I was starting to develop a real need to see what Jack's parents looked like, and we weren't even related.

"Tiffany, could you come in here for a minute?" Mom called from the kitchen.

"Coming, Mom," I said, and left the living room fast. It takes a lot out of you making small talk with a brother.

"What do you think?" Mom whispered as soon as she saw me. "Does he look like me?"

"He has your eyes," I said. "And I think he has your old hair color."

"I know," Mom said, patting her bottle red hair. "I almost asked them to dye me back to my original shade, but I wasn't sure I could remember it anymore. Do you like him? Does he seem nice?"

"Very nice," I said. "Very good manners."

"He sure didn't inherit those from Ronny," Mom declared. "Come on, let's start taking the food out."

So we did. We carried out platters of chicken and mashed potatoes and biscuits and salad. Jack came to the table as soon as he saw what we were doing.

"Oh, no," he said. "I mean, I'm sorry. I should have told you. I'm a vegetarian."

"You are?" Mom said. She looked as shocked as if he'd told her he was a vampire. Meat is very important to Mom. "You're not sick or anything, are you?"

"No, it's for moral reasons," Jack said. "It drives my mom, my mother, her name's Cathy, it drives Cathy crazy."

"Your mom," my mom said. "It would drive me crazy, too, if Tiffany stopped eating meat just for moral reasons."

"Don't worry about it," I told her. "I'll never be that moral."

"There's plenty for me to eat," Jack said. "Potatoes and biscuits and salad."

"The salad has bacon in it," Mom said. "I crumbled bacon in it."

"We can wash the bacon off, can't we Jack?" I said. "You'll eat it if we wash the bacon off, won't you?"

I thought he hesitated for a moment, but then he said, "Of course I can," and for the first time since we'd met, I kind of liked him. I took the salad into the kitchen and washed it all. The salad dressing went the way of the bacon, but we weren't about to complain. At least there'd be something green on Jack's plate. All his other food was gray-white.

Mom hardly ate her chicken, which I figured was out of deference[4] to the vegetarian, but I had two and a half pieces, figuring it might be years before Mom made it again. Jack ate more potatoes than I'd ever seen another human being eat. No gravy, but lots of potatoes. We talked polite stuff during dinner, what he was studying in college, where Mom worked, the adjustments Leigh Ann had had to make. The real things could only be discussed one on one, so after the pie and ice cream, I excused myself and went to Mom's room to watch TV. Only I couldn't make my eyes focus, so I crossed the hall to my room, and recreated my messes. Once I had everything in proper order, though, I put things back the way Mom had had them. I could hear them talking while I moved piles around, and then I turned on my radio, so I couldn't even hear the occasional stray word, like *father* and *high school* and *lawyer*. That was a trick I'd learned years ago, when Mom and Dad were in their fighting stage. The radio played a lot of old songs that night. It made me feel like I was seven all over again.

After a while Mom knocked on my door and said Jack was leaving, so I went to the living room and shook hands with him again. I still couldn't tell anything about his personality from his handshake, but he did have good manners, and he gave me a little pecking kiss on my cheek, which I thought was sweet of him. Mom kept the door open, and watched as he walked the length of the corridor to the stairs. She didn't close the

---

4 **deference:** respect, regard for another's wishes

door until he'd gotten into a car, his I assumed. Maybe it was a loaner from his father.

"You give away a baby," Mom said, "and twenty years later he turns up on your doorstep a vegetarian."

"He turns up a turnip," I said.

But Mom wasn't in the mood for those kinds of jokes. "Don't you ever make that mistake," she said.

"What mistake?" I asked, afraid she meant making jokes. If I couldn't make jokes with Mom, I wouldn't know how to talk with her.

"Don't you ever give up something so important to you that it breathes when you do," Mom said. "It doesn't have to be a kid. It can be a dream, an ambition, or a marriage, or a house. It can be anything you care about as deeply as you care about your own life. Don't ever just give it away, because you'll spend the rest of your life wondering about it, or pretending you don't wonder, which is the same thing, and you'll wake up one morning and realize it truly is gone and a big part of you is gone with it. Do you hear me, Tiffany?"

"I hear you," I said. I'd never seen Mom so intense, and I didn't like being around her. "I'm kind of tired now, Mom. Would you mind if I went to bed early?"

"I'll clean up tomorrow," Mom said. "You can go to bed."

So I did. I left her sitting in the living room and went to my bedroom and closed my door. But this time I didn't turn the radio on, and later, when I'd been lying on my bed for hours, not able to sleep, I could hear her in her room crying. I'd heard her cry in her room a hundred times before, and a hundred times before I'd gotten up and comforted her, and I knew she'd cry a hundred times again, and I'd comfort her then, too, but that night I just stayed in my room, on my bed, staring at the ceiling and listening to her cry. I think I did the right thing, not going in there. That's how it is with strangers. You can never really comfort them. ❧

RESPONDING TO CLUSTER FOUR

ESSENTIAL QUESTION: DOES FAMILY MATTER?

Thinking Skill SYNTHESIZING

The last group of selections in this book provides an opportunity for independent learning and the application of the critical thinking skill, synthesis. *Synthesizing* means examining all the things you have learned from this book and combining them to form a richer and more meaningful view why being part of a family matters.

There are many ways to demonstrate what you know about family. Here are some possibilities. Your teacher may provide others.

1. Break into small groups, with each group taking responsibility for teaching a part of the final cluster. To teach the lesson you might:

   a) create discussion questions and lead a discussion

   b) develop vocabulary activities

   c) prepare a test for the cluster selections

   As you develop your activity, keep the essential question in mind: "Does family matter?"

2. We all know from life experiences that there is no way to avoid problems. How we deal with problems and the decisions we make today influence who we become in the future. From this book, choose the one character you feel would be most able to help someone your age with family problems. Explain your answer.

3. Individually or in small groups, develop an independent project that demonstrates the importance of family. For example, you might give a presentation on parenting techniques, discipline strategies, or coping skills when faced with problems. Other options might include a music video, dance, poem, performance, drama, or artistic rendering.

ACKNOWLEDGMENTS

Text Credits CONTINUED FROM PAGE 2   "Gillian, age Thirteen," from *How It Feels When Parents Divorce* by Jill Krementz. Copyright © 1984 by Jill Krementz. Reprinted by permission of Alfred A. Knopf, Inc.

"Growing Up" from *Baseball in April and Other Stories*, copyright © 1990 by Gary Soto, reprinted by permission of Harcourt Brace & Company.

"I Am Singing Now" by Luci Tapahonso, from *A Breeze Swept Through* . Copyright © 1987 by Luci Tapahonso. Reprinted by permission of West End Press, Albuquerque, New Mexico.

"Keeping Hair" by Ramona Wilson from *Voices of the Rainbow*, edited by Kenneth Rosen. Copyright © 1975, 1993 by Kenneth Rosen. Published by Arcade Publishing, Inc., New York by arrangement with Seaver Books, New York. Reprinted by permission of the publisher.

"Lectures on How You Never Lived Back Home" is from *Her Wild American Self*, a collection of short stories by M. Evelina Galang, Coffee House Press, 1996. Copyright © 1996 M. Evelina Galang. Used by permission of the publisher and author.

"The Nativity" from *Puppies, Dogs and Blue Northers: Reflections on Being Raised by a Pack of Sled Dogs*, copyright © 1996 by Gary Paulsen, reprinted by permission of Harcourt, Inc.

"Nikki-Rosa" from *Black Feeling, Black Talk, Black Judgment* by Nikki Giovanni. Text copyright © 1968, 1970 by Nikki Giovanni. By permission of William Morrow and Company, Inc.

"Phoenix Farm" copyright © 1996 by Jane Yolen; originally published in *Bruce Coville's Book of Magic*, Apple/Scholastic, edited by Bruce Coville. Now appears in *Twelve Impossible Things Before Breakfast*, copyright © 1997 by Jane Yolen, Harcourt Brace & Company. Reprinted by permission of Curtis Brown, Ltd.

"Possibilities," from *Heroes in Disguise* by Linda Pastan. Copyright © 1991 by Linda Pastan. Reprinted by permission of W. W. Norton & Company, Inc.

"Somebody's Son" by Richard Pindell. First published in *American Girl* magazine, August 1966. Reprinted by permission of the author.

"Thanksgiving in Polynesia" by Susan Haven, copyright © 1992 by Susan Haven, from *Funny You Should Ask* by David Gale, Editor. Used by permission of Dell Publishing, a division of Random House, Inc.

"Third Child" by Erma Bombeck. From *Forever, Erma*, copyright © 1996 by the Estate of Erma Bombeck. Reprinted with permission of Andrews and McMeel Publishing. All rights reserved.

"Trust Me" by Frederick Waterman. Taken from *Hemispheres* magazine, December 1998. Copyright © 1998. Reprinted by permission of Frederick Waterman.

Every reasonable effort has been made to properly acknowledge ownership of all material used. Any omissions or mistakes are not intentional and, if brought to the publisher's attention, will be corrected in future editions.

Photo and Art Credits Cover and Title Page: Mary Cassatt, *The Boating Party*, Chester Dale Collection, © 1999, Board of Trustees, National Gallery of Art, Washington DC, 1893/1894, oil on canvas, 35 7/16 x 46 1/8 inches. Page 3, 4-5: (Detail): Edward Hopper, *Adam's House*, 1928. Watercolor on paper, 16 x 25 inches. The Roland P. Murdock Collection, Wichita Art Museum, Wichita, KS. Page 8: Ibid. Page 9: UR, Richard Samuel Roberts. Page 10: © Noble Stock/International Stock. Page 11: Bruce Davidson/© Magnum Photos, Inc. Page 13: © Elma Garcia/Photonica. Page 14: Norman Rockwell, *Freedom from Want*. Printed by permission of the Norman Rockwell Family Trust, copyright ©1943, the Norman Rockwell Family Trust. Page 22: © Preuit Holland/Picturesque Stock Photos. Page 24-25: Koji Yamashita/© Panoramic Images. Page 26: Ruth Wright Paulsen. Pages 29, 33: Illustrations copyright ©1996 by Ruth Wright Paulsen. From *Puppies, Dogs and Blue Northers* by Gary Paulsen, Harcourt Brace Publishers. Page 34: Gordon Parks. Pages 38-39: Bruce Davidson/ © Magnum Photos, Inc. Page 45: © Elma Garcia/Photonica. Page 46: Duane Michals, (Detail) *What is Memory?* Page 55: Mary Cassatt, *Girl Arranging Her Hair*, 1886. Oil on canvas, 29 5/8 x 24 5/8 inches. National Gallery of Art, Washington DC, Chester Dale Collection. Page 56: Robert Knopes/Omni-Photo Communications. Page 60: Mark Harme/© Tony Stone Images. Pages 62, 63, 64, and 65: Nick Kelsh. Page 66: Catherine Karnow/ Corbis. Page 75: Joseph Deal. Page 77: Camille Tokerud/© Tony Stone Images. Page 78: Index Stock. Pages 84-85: Art Wolfe/© Tony Stone Images. Pages 86, 88: From *How It Feels When Parents Divorce* by Jill Krementz. Copyright © 1984 by Jill Krementz, reprinted by permission of Alfred A. Knopf, Inc. Page 93: Tarleton Blackwell, *Hog Series CXXXV; Cinderella Section XVIX*, 1995. Graphite, prismacolor and watercolor, 20 x 16 inches. Courtesy Lewallen Gallery, Santa Fe. Page 103: Super Stock. Page 104, 109: Rodica Prato. Page 111: Arvind Garg/© Tony Stone Images. Page 112: William Burlingham. Page 116: Alice Neel, *Moose*, 1956. Oil on canvas, 36 x 26 inches. Courtesy Robert Miller Gallery, NY. Page 125: Nicholas DeVore/© Tony Stone Images. Pages 126-127: Jeremy Walker/© Tony Stone Images. Page 128: Treleven Photography. Page 132: © Andy Sacks/TSW-Click/Chicago, Ltd. Page 135: William Burlingham.